Geometry Activities from Many Cultures

Beatrice Lumpkin

J. WESTON
WALCH
PUBLISHER
Portland, Maine

User's Guide
to
Walch Reproducible Books

As part of our general effort to provide educational materials that are as practical and economical as possible, we have designated this publication a "reproducible book." The designation means that purchase of the book includes purchase of the right to limited reproduction of all pages on which this symbol appears:

Here is the basic Walch policy: We grant to individual purchasers of this book the right to make sufficient copies of reproducible pages for use by all students of a single teacher. This permission is limited to a single teacher, and does not apply to entire schools or school systems so institutions purchasing the book should pass the permission on to a single teacher. Copying of the book or its parts for resale is prohibited.

Any questions regarding this policy or requests to purchase further reproduction rights should be addressed to:

Permissions Editor
J. Weston Walch, Publisher
321 Valley Street • P. O. Box 658
Portland, Maine 04104-0658

1   2   3   4   5   6   7   8   9   10

ISBN 0-8251-3285-1

Contents

unit 1 (handwritten)
Unit 10 (handwritten)
Unit 8 (handwritten)
Unit 6 (handwritten)
Unit 7 (handwritten)
✓ (handwritten, item 7)
✓ (handwritten, item 19)
✓ (handwritten, item 24)
PROJECT / EXTRA CREDIT (handwritten, item 26)
1st HALF (handwritten, item 30)
GOOD STORY ? (handwritten, item 31)

Unit 2

Introduction

GOALS

This book provides student-ready multicultural materials for the geometry classroom. The goals of this book are:

1. To enrich the geometry curriculum with real-life examples from many cultures, including African American, Latino, Native American, Pacific Islander, and Asian American—cultures underrepresented in the high school curriculum.

2. To help students gain pride in their own heritage and to learn respect for other cultures.

The National Standards movement helped inspire this book by calling for the connection of mathematics to real-life situations. As pointed out in *Curriculum and Evaluation Standards for School Mathematics* (page 157), "Prior to the work of the ancient Greeks . . . geometric ideas were tied directly to the solution of real-world problems." Some of the real-world problems that are solved in this book make natural connections between geometry and other subjects, including art, science, architecture, clothing design, and engineering.

SCOPE OF THE BOOK

Geometry may well be the oldest of the sciences because people have always worked with patterns of lines and shapes. The first chapter of the book presents a timeline chronicling exciting discoveries in geometric thinking. Then, a substantial chapter on the geometry of multicultural art introduces students to transformations and the concept of motion in geometry. These examples from many cultures feature some of the newest ideas in geometry, such as fractals. This chapter also provides opportunities for hands-on activities and projects.

There are many examples and activities based on the achievements of ancient civilizations from Egypt, Babylonia, China, and India, to the Americas and the Pacific Islands. The methods of these early civilizations often involved proof by construction. Construction proofs lend themselves to classroom use and are in line with the emphasis on manipulatives and activities. By following in the footsteps of ancient mathematicians, students will gain confidence in their own mathematical ability.

Although Euclid's work is not directly presented in this book, the multicultural aspect of Euclidian geometry should be noted. His books were all written in Alexandria, Egypt. The written record does not place him outside of Africa, not even for a visit. From Euclid's death to the death of Hypatia, 700 years later, Alexandria was the center of the Hellenistic world, including parts of North Africa, Southern Europe, and Western Asia.

The traditional belief is that the Greeks learned geometry from the ancient Egyptians. Egyptians were credited with developing geometry in order to redraw farm boundaries after the annual Nile River floods had washed away boundary markers. Several units in this book are based on the geometry that arose to solve problems caused by the Nile floods. The ancient civilizations of Mesopotamia, India, and China also made massive contributions to the science of geometry. Their contributions represent much of the content of this book.

STRUCTURE OF THE BOOK

As an aid to integrating multicultural material into the geometry sequence, the topics in this book follow the standard textbook sequence. These topics are geometry in art, measurement, area and volume; circles; similarity; right triangles; and trigonometry. Additional cultural material appears in chapters on map making and architecture. Units for each topic open with one or two pages of reading about the geometric achievement of the culture, followed by Questions for Critical Thinking. Activities and projects complete each unit.

A bibliography for further reading is supplied at the end of the book to stimulate teacher and student research.

AUTHOR'S NOTE

Many teachers, writers, and organizations are participating in the rediscovery of multicultural geometry. I would like to thank the Benjamin Banneker Association of mathematics teachers and its founders, including Dorothy Strong and William Greer, for helping to create a climate in which multiculturalism can flourish. I am indebted to Ron Eglash for his field research on the applications of fractal concepts to traditional art in Africa, and to Claudia Zaslavsky for helpful suggestions for the chapter on symmetry. Of course, any errors that may occur are mine alone.

Background of Geometry

Timeline for Geometry: Multicultural Highlights

Reproducible 1

PROCEDURE

1. Distribute the handout and ask students to study it.
2. Divide the class into four groups—one to measure the perimeter of the classroom, another to choose a scale for the timeline, a third to attach the timeline to the walls, and a fourth to tape the timeline to the walls.
3. Provide one copy of the timeline to cut into separate slips.
4. Put the slips into a bowl, and have each student choose one or more, depending on the size of the class.

5. Proceed as directed in step 4 of the handout.

EXTENSION

For an optional extension of this activity, students or groups of students could do further research on timeline topics that interest them.

Drama in the Service of Mathematics

Reproducible 2

PROCEDURE

Divide the class into groups and distribute the handout. Have students write short plays based on the scenarios from the handout (or they may invent their own scenarios).

Background of Geometry

Timeline for Geometry: Multicultural High Points

MATERIALS

adding machine tape
scissors
large bowl
felt-tipped pens
meterstick
masking tape
map of the world

Check off each step as you complete it.

❑ 1. Study the timeline on the following pages. What is the time span covered by the dates on the timeline?

❑ 2. Different groups will measure the perimeter of your classroom, choose a scale for the time-line, mark the tape with the dates, and attach the timeline to the walls with masking tape. If necessary, the timeline can go around the room several times. Cut apart one copy of the timeline, and put slips in a bowl.

❑ 3. Each student, in turn, selects a timeline entry from the bowl.

❑ 4. Starting at 150,000 B.P., the student with the next item in the time sequence will announce her or his item, locate the country on the world map, and then tape the entry on the time-line. The abbreviation B.C.E. (Before the Common Era) is used instead of B.C.

Note: Prehistoric dates are given as years before the present, or B.P. These are approximate dates; some are still under debate.

Timeline for Geometry	
150,000 B.P.:	Modern humans (Homo sapiens sapiens) have developed in Africa. In Kenya, people were using geometric thinking to make carefully shaped tool blades.
90,000 B.P.:	Africans in Zaire were using toothed harpoons. People had a mental picture of the geometric shape they wanted before they made the toothed harpoons.
40,000 B.P. or earlier:	Australian rock paintings show that people were using geometric ideas in art. To reach Australia by boat required planning and knowledge of navigation.

(continued)

Geometry Activities from Many Cultures

Timeline for Geometry: Multicultural High Points *(continued)*

37,000 B.P.:	Tally records with 29 notches were carved in South Africa and other places.
33,000 B.P.:	A mine with pits and underground galleries in Southern Egypt allowed large-scale production of tool-grade flints. A teen-age miner was buried there with his mining tool.
25,000 B.P.:	Ishango fossil bone in Central Africa shows tallies for 2 and 4, 3 and 6, 10, 5 and 5, and other numbers. These groups of numbers were thought to show multiplication by 2 or a record of phases of the moon.
6000 B.P.:	In Nubia (Sudan and Southern Egypt) there is evidence of the use of sailboats, scales, and weights. Standard weights show early use of proportions.
4241 B.C.E. (some claim 2773 B.C.E.):	The first solar calendar was developed in Egypt, based on a study of star positions. Early astronomy depended on geometry.
3000 B.C.E.:	Egyptian Pharaoh Narmer used numerals above 1,000,000. Early cuneiform numerals used in Mesopotamia.
2700 to 2600 B.C.E.:	Geometry and arithmetic were developed for construction of large stone structures in Egypt. Rectangular coordinates were used for pyramid plans, and guidelines using a zero symbol were used as a reference for above ground and below ground levels.
2500 B.C.E.:	Geometry, standard measures, writing, and numerals were used in India to plan cities and to build large brick structures in the Harrapan civilization.
1900 B.C.E.:	Algebraic equations and geometric formulas were used in Egypt and Babylonia. A Babylonian tablet lists values for sides of right triangles, 1300 years before Pythagoras.
1400 B.C.E.:	Writing, including oracle-bone numerals, developed in China.
700 B.C.E.:	Sulbasutras were written in India, giving brick masons exact instructions for building altars. The sulbasutras used the right triangle theorem and basic principles of geometry.
550 B.C.E.:	The *Chou Pei Suan Ching*, a Chinese mathematics book, contained an old Chinese proof of the right-triangle theorem. The theorem was known in China before Pythagoras.
585 to 540 B.C.E.:	Thales and Pythagoras studied in Egypt, then brought Egyptian Geometry to the Greek Islands. Pythagoras founded a school of philosophy, music, and mathematics.

(continued)

Timeline for Geometry: Multicultural High Points *(continued)*

300 B.C.E.:	Euclid of Alexandria, Egypt, collected the best work of Greek, African and Asian mathematicians and compiled *The Elements*, a model Geometry textbook.
230 B.C.E.:	In Egypt, Eratosthenes used geometry to calculate the circumference of the earth.
36 B.C.E.:	Maya and other Central American cultures invented place-value numerals and a zero placeholder. Their massive pyramid cities show geometric planning.
150:	Ptolemy, in Egypt, wrote his great work on astronomy, using trigonometry.
250:	Liu Hui, in China, explained the geometric principles needed for surveying.
415:	Hypatia of Alexandria, the first woman mathematician-scientist whose name we know, was murdered. She is remembered for her work in geometry, algebra, and engineering.
603 to 686:	A zero symbol was used in place-value numerals in Cambodia and Indonesia.
800–1400:	Al-Khwarizmi and Umar al-Khayyami (Omar Khayyam) in Central Asia, and Abu Kamil in Africa are among scholars who restored and went beyond Euclid's geometry. Trigonometry was developed in India and greatly expanded by Islamic mathematicians.
1000:	Native American Mississippi culture built huge geometric mounds and pyramids.
1200:	Geometric planning was used in Zimbabwe to build great stone structures and walls for centers of a powerful African empire based on mining, agriculture, and trade.
1400:	Latin translations of Islamic books on geometry, algebra, science and philosophy helped inspire the European Renaissance.
1500's:	Aztec governments in Mexico used advanced methods to measure land area. Wealth taken from the Americas fueled the Industrial Revolution in Europe.
1680's:	In Europe, Newton and Leibniz combined integral and differential calculus. Some difficult geometric problems were easily solved with calculus.
1700 to 1999:	Mathematics and science grew explosively in Europe and North America. Africa, Asia, Central and South America, once great centers of mathematics, lost ground during centuries of colonialism. They are now fighting their way back up to the top.
2000:	We are working to make the twenty-first century better!

Geometry Activities from Many Cultures

Drama in the Service
of Mathematics

Write a scenario for a short play or skit that you can present to the class. Select from the following topics of science and mathematics, or use a topic of your own, with your teacher's approval.

1. Building a round house

Imagine you are living in a cave 20,000 years ago. You decide to move to an area with good hunting, but there are no caves nearby. So you plan to build a house and you decide to make it a round house. Write a scenario on how you could draw a circle for the floor and how big a circle you would need.

2. Inventing bricks

You're living ten thousand years ago in a round house made of reeds. The reeds came from a nearby river bank where the soil is rich with clay. You try plastering your reed house with clay. The house stays cooler in the day and warmer at night. Write a play about that experience and how that might lead to using clay bricks for your next house.

3. Building a rectangular house

You're living seven thousand years ago and have prepared sun-baked bricks that are about 30 cm ($11\frac{13}{16}$") long, and 15 cm ($5\frac{29}{32}$") high. You want to be sure the first row of bricks outlines a rectangular shape. Write a scenario on how you could test that the floor has the shape of a rectangle. How many bricks will you need?

4. Invention of agriculture

It is thought that women were the first to invent agriculture because they were food gatherers. Show how the invention of agriculture might have happened.

Hint: Suppose ancient food-gatherers accidentally dropped some wild grain.

5. Sailboats

The earliest drawing of a sailboat comes from Nubia, south of Egypt. How do you think people got the idea of using boats and putting sails on boats?

Hints: Suppose a swimmer held on to floating reeds. Could that give someone the idea of rafts? But the top of a raft gets wet. How could that be avoided? You happened to hold up your shirt or a branch which caught the wind. Would that give you any ideas?

6. Building the pyramids

Your group is a team of architects at a building site for a pyramid 5000 years ago. Write a play about planning the construction of a pyramid.

Geometry Activities from Many Cultures

Geometry in Multicultural Art

Symmetry: Rotational

Reproducible 4

ANSWERS FOR REPRODUCIBLE 4

1. 120°
2. 240°
3. No answer needed
4. Rotational symmetry at 90°, 180°, 270°, 360°; also, 4 axes of symmetry

Symmetry: What Kind?

Reproducible 5

ANSWERS

Axes and Angles		
Figure	# of axes of symmetry	Angles of rotation, degrees
1	0	90, 180, 270, 360
2	2	180, 360
3	4	90, 180, 270, 360
4	0	72, 144, 216, 288, 360
5	0	360

3. Sum of lengths of two small semi-circles = the length of the large semicircle.

4.

Symmetry of Geometric Shapes		
	No. Axes of Symmetry	Angles of rotation, degrees
(a)	3	120, 240, 360
(b)	0	360
(c)	4	90, 180, 270, 360
(d)	4	180, 360
(e)	6	60, 120, 180, 240, 300, 360
(f)	infinite	Infinite number, all from 0 to 360

Geometric Transformations in Border Patterns

Reproducible 6

PROCEDURE

1. Distribute the handout, and have students answer questions 1 to 3. Divide the class into groups of four.
2. Discuss glide reflection and ask students to sketch their own strip patterns.
3. Have groups choose their favorite designs to copy onto poster paper for class display.

ANSWERS

1. (a) Answers will vary.
   (b) Answers will vary.
   (c) Basic design is nonsymmetric.
2. 3 cm
3. Answers will vary.

Tilings: The Multicultural Forerunners of M.C. Escher

Reproducible 7

PROCEDURE

Distribute the handout. As a group, try to fit the Islamic-style tilings together to form a tessellation.

ANSWERS

Regular Polygons			
	No. of Sides	m vertex angle	Can tile space?
Triangle	3	60°	yes
Square	4	90°	yes
Pentagon	5	108°	no
Hexagon	6	120°	yes
Heptagon	7	$128\frac{4}{7}°$	no
Octagon	8	135°	no
Nonagon	9	140°	no
Decagon	10	144°	no

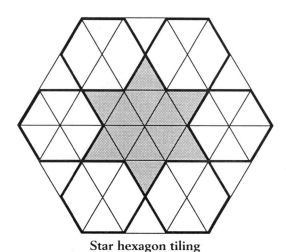

Star hexagon tiling

Tilings: Pattern from the Alhambra

Reproducible 8

PROCEDURE

1. Distribute the handout.
2. Have students make a Moorish tessellation with curved tiles, using the diagrams on the handout as a guide.
3. As a class, paste the individual tiles to a piece of poster paper to form a tessellation.

Networks from Africa

Reproducible 9

Fractals: The Multicultural Connection

Reproducible 10

THE BAMANA AND THE CANTOR SET: ANSWERS TO QUESTIONS FOR CRITICAL THINKING

2. Sierpinski triangle: removal of interior triangles continues infinitely. The number of triangles in the Mauritanian design is finite.

Symmetry: Reflectional

The love of art unites all cultures and all human history. Humans share a universal sense of beauty, color, form, and symmetry. Form and symmetry are also important in the study of mathematics.

In a symmetric design, the figure can be flipped across a line or turned a given angle without changing its size or shape. The idea of symmetry also applies to our own bodies. We think of our faces as near symmetric, comparing left and right sides. We say that our face has a vertical axis of symmetry. This textile design from the Sahel in North Africa has a horizontal axis of symmetry.

Vertical Axis of Symmetry

**Textile from the Sahel
Horizontal Axis of Symmetry**

You can use a mirror to check the reflectional symmetry of a design. Place a flat mirror on edge on an axis of symmetry of a design. The mirror will reflect an image identical to the half of the design behind the mirror. That is why this type of symmetry is called **reflectional**.

Some designs have more than one axis of symmetry. Of course, there are also beautiful designs that are not symmetric. Learning how to classify symmetries is useful because it is a way to study the effect of motions in geometry. Here are some designs from America and Africa that show different kinds of symmetry. Some even combine different kinds of symmetry.

**Lightning
Teton Dakota
Horizontal Axis of Symmetry**

**Belt design,
Botswana
Vertical Axis of Symmetry**

**Good luck
Asante
4 Axes of Symmetry: Vertical,
Horizontal and 2 Diagonal**

**Bird—Teton Dakota
No Symmetry**

(continued)

Geometry Activities from Many Cultures

Symmetry: Reflectional *(continued)*

Critical Thinking

1. Use a mirror to test the lines you believe are axes of symmetry in the following designs. Then use a pencil and straightedge to draw the axes of reflectional symmetry.

Sculptured Clay Wall Reliefs, Nigeria

Woven Mat, Lower Congo   Swazi Basket, after Gerdes, 95

Bushoong Embroidery, Congo-Kinshasa

(continued)

Geometry Activities from Many Cultures

Symmetry: Reflectional *(continued)*

2. Draw a design that has only a vertical axis of symmetry.

3. Draw a design that has only a horizontal axis of symmetry.

4. Draw a design that has vertical and horizontal axes of symmetry.

5. Some figures, such as regular hexagons, have several axes of symmetry. Recall that a line is called an axis of symmetry if a design, reflected around that line, coincides with the original design. In the figure below, draw all of the axes of symmetry of the hexagon.

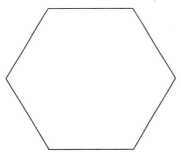

6. Draw a design that does not have reflectional symmetry.

Geometry Activities from Many Cultures

Symmetry: Rotational

These beautiful Egyptian bowl designs go back to about 3500 B.C.E. The hippopotamus bowl has three circular parts to the design, each with a different symmetry. With the mirror test, you can find 14 axes of symmetry for the outer ring of waves. There are seven axes through the peaks, and seven more through the troughs. But in the reflections, a hippopotamus appears to have two heads or two tails!

However, the ring with three hippopotamuses has another type of symmetry, called rotational symmetry. Explore the rotational symmetry of the hippopotamus design.

Prehistoric Egyptian Bowl Designs
after Eva Wilson, 1986

Check off each step as you complete it.

❑   1. With the point of your pen, fix a point at the center of the design. Then slowly turn the design, counterclockwise, until the picture of the hippopotamuses coincides with the original design. The angle of rotation is _____.

❑   2. Continue the rotation until the picture again coincides with the original design. The total angle of rotation is now _____.

❑   3. Continue the rotation until the picture again coincides with the original design. The total angle of rotation is 360° and the picture is back to its original position.

❑   4. Repeat steps 1 and 2 to explore the symmetry of the other bowl design above. Does this bowl have reflectional symmetry as well as rotational symmetry?

Geometry Activities from Many Cultures

Name _____

Date _____

Symmetry: What Kind?

Directions: Use a mirror, turn the page around the design center, or use any other aid that will help you find the types of symmetry in these designs. Fill out the following table, giving the number of axes of symmetry for designs with reflectional symmetry. For rotational symmetry, list angles of rotation at which the design coincides with the original.

1. Ghana, West Africa

2. Tanzania, Southeast Africa

3. Pima, southwestern United States

4. Mescalero Apache, southwestern United States

5. Ghana, West Africa

Complete the table

Axes and Angles		
Figure	**No. of Axes of Symmetry**	**Angles of Rotation**
1		
2		
3		
4		
5		

(continued)

Geometry Activities from Many Cultures

Symmetry: What Kind? *(continued)*

Questions for Critical Thinking

1. Make a simple design that has exactly two perpendicular axes of reflectional symmetry. Test your design for rotational symmetry. At what angles of rotation do you find rotational symmetry?

2. With the aid of your compass, make a "yin-yang" design after the small Chinese model shown here. Does it have reflectional symmetry? Rotational symmetry?

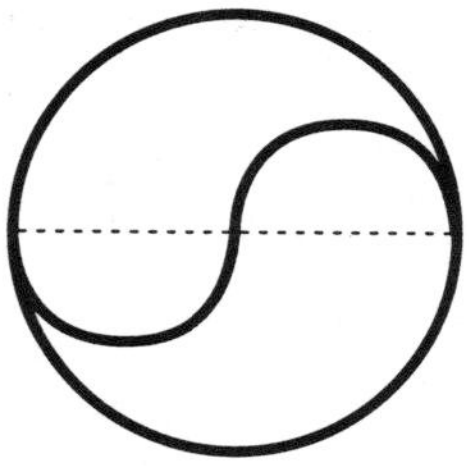

    Use a separate sheet of paper. Follow these steps:

    (a) Construct a circle. Lightly pencil in a diameter.

    (b) Bisect the radius, half of the diameter you penciled in above. At the midpoint of the radius, use half of the radius to construct a semicircle below the diameter. At the other half of the diameter, construct a semicircle above the other half of the diameter. Erase the diameter.

3. Compare the lengths of the two small semicircles and the large semicircle.

4. On a sheet of isometric grid paper, draw the following figures:

    (a) equilateral triangle

    (b) scalene triangle

    (c) square

    (d) nonsquare rectangle

    (e) regular hexagon

    (f) circle

    Test for reflectional and rotational symmetry. Fill in the table.

Symmetry of Geometric Shapes		
	Number of Axes of Symmetry	**Rotational Symmetry/ Angles of Rotation**
(a) Equilateral triangle		
(b) Scalene triangle		
(c) Square		
(d) Non-square rectangle		
(e) Regular hexagon		
(f) Circle		

© 1997 Beatrice Lumpkin
J. Weston Walch, Publisher

Geometry Activities from Many Cultures

Geometric Transformations in Border Patterns

Traditional art in all parts of the world often takes the form of border designs, or strip patterns, used to decorate pottery, clothing, and homes. Border patterns start with a design unit. Then the design is repeated across the strip by using geometric motions, or transformations.

Designing a strip pattern requires mathematical measurement and use of transformations. Studying and creating these designs is fun and a good way to learn about transformations in geometry. Border designs from all over the world show that all people have developed mathematical skills.

TRANSLATION

The motions, or transformations, that move the design unit across the strip are called rigid, or *isometric*. That is because the size and shape of the design remain the same. One way to repeat a design is to translate, or move the design unit, across to the next space on the strip. In the following two strips, translation is the only way to repeat the design. Do you know why?

Bushoong, Central Africa

Chitimacha, Native American

REFLECTION

Designs that have internal symmetry can be reflected, or turned. The lotus design in this border from an Egyptian tomb has vertical reflectional symmetry. A vertical line down the center of the lotus will reflect the left side to the right side. Another reflection will move the lotus generator design to the next space in the border.

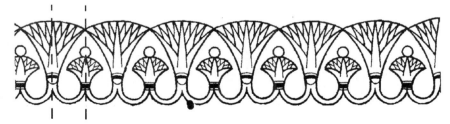

(continued)

Geometry Activities from Many Cultures

Geometric Transformations in Border Patterns *(continued)*

The following triangular pattern from a prehistoric Egyptian bowl is another example of motion, or transformation, by vertical reflection. The pattern also provides proof that there was irrigation 5500 years ago in Egypt. The small squares are a symbol for irrigated land.

GLIDE REFLECTION

Some early artists must have noticed the pattern that footprints make in the sand. As the toes of the left foot push down, the right foot comes forward. That is a translation, moving across a strip. But the right footprint is a reflection of the left footprint. The pattern of combined translation and horizontal reflection is called a *glide reflection*. This pattern has produced some of the most pleasing border designs.

Here are two examples from cultures thousands of miles apart. The first is from the San Ilde-fonso pueblo culture of New Mexico. The second is from the Bakuba culture of Central Africa. Study these designs.

From the Santo Domingo pueblo

From the Bakuba of Central Africa, adapted from D. W. Crowe, 1971

Critical Thinking

1. The design unit, or generator, of a border pattern is the part of the repeating pattern that does not have symmetry. For the previously illustrated Asante and Seminole patterns:

   (a) Draw the generator of the Bushoong pattern.

   (b) Draw the generator of the Chitimacha pattern.

   (c) Why is translation the only way to take the Chitimacha design unit across a strip?

(continued)

Geometry Activities from Many Cultures

Geometric Transformations in Border Patterns *(continued)*

2. The generator of the prehistoric Egyptian design illustrated previously is half of the isosceles triangle. (Notice that the triangle is not equilateral.)

1.5 cm

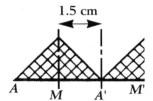

1.5 cm

A   M   A'   M'

Reflect the half-triangle through the vertical line. Point *M* has not moved. Point *A* was on the left of the vertical line but its image, *A'*, is on the right of the vertical line. Now reflect the half-triangle again through the second vertical line. Point *M* has moved to *M'*. How far has point *M* been carried across, or translated?

_____

3. Draw a small, nonsymmetric design. Repeat it by translation to make a border pattern.

4. Make individual strip patterns using glide reflection. Discuss and approve each design before it is repeated across the strip. Then make a poster displaying all the patterns.

© 1997 Beatrice Lumpkin
J. Weston Walch, Publisher

Geometry Activities from Many Cultures

Tiling: The Multicultural Forerunners of M. C. Escher

Scarcely a geometry book is printed these days without artwork by Maurits Cornelis Escher (1898–1972). If many of his tiling designs recall the tile patterns of the Alhambra palace, that is not by accident. Escher spent ten years in Spain and Italy. For much of that time, he studied the art of the Alhambra palace complex in Granada, Spain. The Alhambra was built by Islamic Africans who ruled parts of Spain from 711 to 1492.

The Islamic culture included artists and mathematicians of different religions. Most were Muslim, but many Jews and Christians also contributed to Islamic culture.

Tilings, or tessellations, are repetitive designs that cover a space, without gaps or overlaps. Where the corners, or vertices, of the tiles meet, the sum of the angles must equal 360°.

The Islamic tilings were based on Euclid's geometry at a time when geometry was no longer studied in most of Europe. Many of the beautiful tiling patterns in the Alhambra start with one simple polygon or a combination of polygons.

Investigate the following regular polygons to see if they can tile or tessellate a space. Use the fact that the sum of the angles at each vertex must be 360°. Regular polygons are equilateral and equiangular.

Doorway, Great Mosque in
Dakar, Senegal

	Regular Polygons		
	Number of Sides	**m vertex angle**	**Can tile space?**
triangle	3	60°	yes
square			
pentagon			
hexagon			
heptagon			
octagon			
nonagon			
decagon			

(continued)

Name _____

Date _____

Tiling: The Multicultural
Forerunners of M. C. Escher *(continued)*

Islamic tilings began with a grid of equilateral triangles or squares. These grids were also tiles, or tessellations, because the triangles or squares covered the space without overlaps or empty spaces. To make these grids, the Islamic artists used a compass. To make your own tessellations, follow this model.

EQUILATERAL TRIANGLE GRID

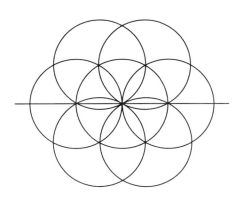

Check off each step as you complete it.

❑ 1. Draw a straight line near the center of your page. Construct a circle with a center on this line. Keep the compass open for the same radius throughout this project.

❑ 2. Construct two more circles, centered at the intersections of the circle with the line.

❑ 3. Construct four more circles, centered at the intersections of the circles.

❑ 4. With a straightedge, connect the center and the six points of the flower formed inside the center circle. This is the start of your equilateral triangle grid.

Note: Islamic artists continued this process until the equilateral triangles covered their space. More complex patterns can be designed on this grid.

❑ 5. On the equilateral triangle grid to the right, color in a six-point star near the center of the grid. The star will have one triangle for each of the six points, and six for the hexagon-shaped center of the star.

❑ 6. With a different color, fill in the six hexagons around the star, one between each pair of star points. Continue to fill in the space, moving out from the center.

Forming a Grid of Equilateral Triangles after *Mathematics of Islamic Art*, Metropolitan Museum of Art, 1975

Geometry Activities from Many Cultures

Name _____

Date _____

Tiling from the Alhambra

Motion in geometry was used by the first African and Asian artists who repeated a pattern on a rock painting or piece of pottery. The curved-tile tessellation from the Alhambra that you will construct uses rotation to repeat the pattern.

Curved-tile tessellations start with a polygon. One or more curved areas are cut out of one side and attached to the opposite side of the polygon. Below are instructions for copying a pattern from the Alhambra that is based on the equilateral triangle.

Project: Make a Moorish tessellation with curved tiles. Check off each step as you complete it.

MATERIALS

equilateral-triangle grid,
paper, paste, scissors

❏ 1. Paste an equilateral triangle grid on card stock. Then outline a triangle with sides that are eight units long at the center of an equilateral triangle grid. Draw the three medians. See Figure 1.

❏ 2. Draw a small equilateral triangle, with sides that are two units long, around the intersection of the medians. Lightly pencil in the squares on the sides of this triangle. See Figure 2.

❏ 3. Draw a six-point star, using these squares as guides. See Figure 3.

❏ 4. With your compass, draw circular arcs to pass through points labeled *A, B, C.* If you wish, you can draw a freehand curve. See Figure 4.

Note: Moorish artists found the exact center of the circle that passes through points *A, B,* and *C.* The center was the point of intersection of the perpendicular bisectors of segments $\overline{AB}$ and $\overline{BC}$.

❏ 5. Cut out the section between the arc *ABC* and the segment $\overline{AC}$. Use it as a template to add a curved section just below *C.* See Figure 5. Save the cutout to use as a template in the next step.

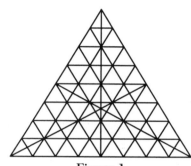

Figure 1

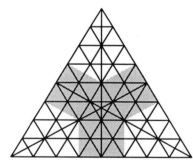

Figure 2

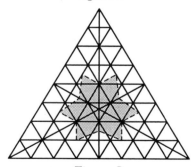

Figure 3

(continued)

© 1997 Beatrice Lumpkin
J. Weston Walch, Publisher

Geometry Activities from Many Cultures

Tiling: Curved Pattern from the Alhambra *(continued)*

❑ 6. On the other two sides of the triangle, use the template to alternately remove and add curved sections as shown in Figure 6. Cut out the center star or make a separate star template. See Figure 7.

❑ 7. Paste your completed tile templates on a piece of poster board. Use Figure 8 as a guide for drawing around the templates to form tiles, then arranging the individual tiles to form a tessellation.

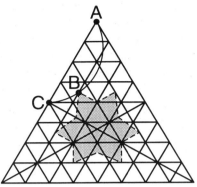

Figure 4

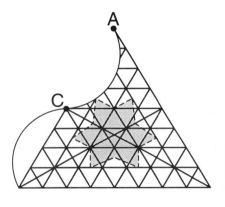

Figure 5

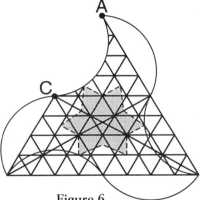

Figure 6

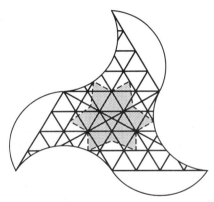

Figure 7

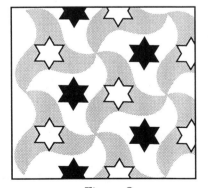

Figure 8
A curved-tile tessellation from the Alhambra after K. Critchlow, 1983

Geometry Activities from Many Cultures

Networks from Africa

Artists in Angola, Zaire, and the Pacific Islands learned to solve network problems hundreds of years ago. Networks are connections, or paths, between objects. They have many applications to science. These applications include not only connections between atoms but also traffic connections. In art, networks have produced many beautiful designs.

AFRICAN TRACINGS

A scholar visiting Zaire was challenged by a Bushong child. "Can you do that?" the child asked after he made a drawing in the sand (Figure 1). This type of drawing is known as a traceable path, because the young artist did not lift his finger or retrace any line. When the scholar could not complete the path, the onlookers laughed. What was it the Bushong knew and the visiting scholar did not know?

Challenge: Trace the drawing in Figure 1. The trick is to enter and exit at the right points. Then try Figure 2.

Figure 1

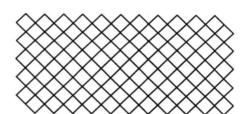

Figure 2

In Northeastern Angola, among the Chokwe people, making sand drawings was a big social event. The artists told a story as they worked. Can you trace the following drawings without lifting your pencil or retracing your path?

**Creeping Vine
after Gerdes, 1987**

adaptation of drawing: **The Path to Truth**

(continued)

Geometry Activities from Many Cultures

Name _____

Date _____

Networks from Africa *(continued)*

Network drawings were called sona (singular, lusona) by the Chokwe of Angola. Geometry was used to plan the drawings. For one type of lusona, the first step is to make an array of dots, with one column more than the number of rows. Then make a traceable path that encloses each dot with one loop. In general, move diagonally as far down, then as far up as possible. Here is a series of sona with one left for you to complete.

1 row, 2 columns

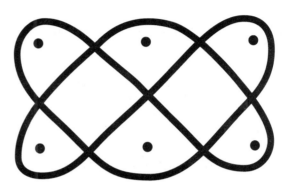

2 rows, 3 columns

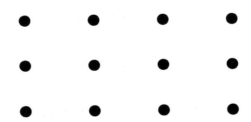

3 rows, 4 columns

Make your own lusona drawing.

Geometry Activities from Many Cultures

Fractals: The Multicultural Connection

The study of fractals is one of the newest fields in geometry. Yet there are many examples in nature that show some of the properties of fractals. Common plants such as ferns and broccoli have self-similarity. The branches have branches, have branches, and so on, all of the same shape. Africans have used this concept in their art for thousands of years.

The earliest African examples come from the capitals, or tops of Egyptian columns. They show symbols for the opening of the lotus blossom, an early Egyptian picture of the creation of life. The following example is from Philae, a Nile River island. Napoleon's Expedition brought this picture to Europe in their report, *Description de L'Egypte*. Notice the startling resemblance to the Cantor set diagram.

Egyptian column

Mathematicians consider the Cantor set a simple, basic fractal. George Cantor (1845–1918) suggested a set that would result from the following operation on the 0 to 1 interval of the real number line, including the end points.

Divide the line interval in thirds and remove the middle interval. The two end thirds remain. Then for each of these end intervals, "Divide the interval in thirds and remove the middle interval." For each of the remaining intervals, "Divide the interval in thirds and remove the middle interval."

Continue to remove the middle third.
Cantor set

Repeat.

Did George Cantor see pictures of the Egyptian columns before he conceived the set shown above? We don't know, but it is a possibility, because Cantor's cousin was a student of Egyptology. Although the Egyptian design looks like the Cantor set, there is one big difference. The repetition of the Cantor set is infinite, while the Egyptian design is finite.

Group Discussion

Would the Cantor set still produce a fractal if instead of the middle third, the middle fifth of the line interval were removed at each step?

(continued)

Fractals: The Multicultural Connection *(continued)*

THE DIVINERS AND THE ANTHROPOLOGIST

An anthropologist from California was studying the mathematics used by the Bamana of Senegal and Mali. Mathematical rules were used to guide Bamana divination. Divination is a combination of counseling and fortune-telling. But the diviners would not reveal their secret methods for any amount of money. Then Eglash, the anthropologist, tried another approach. He told them about the Cantor set. The head diviner became very excited. "Tell that man what he wants to know," the head diviner decided.

What was it about the Cantor set that excited the head diviner? It was the resemblance of Cantor's methods to the methods used by the Bamana. Both used a special kind of repetition, called iteration. The result of the first step is the start of the second step. The output of the second step is the input to the third step, and so on. Iteration is also used in the design of fractals. The people of Mauritania used a repeating design of triangles, as shown above the doorway pictured here. This design, if repeated indefinitely, is called the Sierpinski triangle fractal.

Mauritanian doorway
after Eglash, 1996

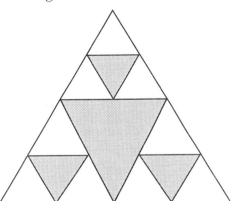

Sierpinski triangle fractal
Connect the midpoints of the sides of each triangle to form
new, smaller triangles. Remove the new triangles.

Questions for Critical Thinking

1. Mark the above diagram to show the next step, the next repetition. Use dark shading to show triangular areas that are removed.

2. Describe the rule for the Mauritanian design. How does the Mauritanian design differ from the Sierpinski triangle fractal?

Geometry Activities from Many Cultures

Measurement: Area and Volume

Measures in Ancient India

Reproducible 13

ANSWERS

1. (a) $P = (40 \times 2 + 24 \times 2) = 128$ bricks
   (b) to line the bath, $128 \times (2440/150) = 128 \times 17 = 2176$ bricks
2. (a) No, $2104/10$, does not equal $2005/10$
   (b) Building to floor space ratios are 2.14, 2.41, 2.21, almost proportional.
   (c) The Lothal warehouse appears to have served a larger region than Lothal.

The Nile Floods and the Birth of Geometry

Reproducible 15

ANSWERS

1. (b) $100{,}000$ cubits^2
   (c) $27{,}562.5$ m^2
2. (b) $200{,}000$ cubits^2
   (c) $A = \frac{1}{2}\,bh$
   (d) Answers will vary.

More Area Examples from the Ah'mose Papyrus

Reproducible 16

ANSWERS

1. (a) $1{,}000{,}000$ square cubits

(b) $A = \frac{1}{2}\,h(b_1 + b_2)$
2. length = 4, width = 3

Surface Area of a Step Pyramid

Reproducible 17

ANSWERS

Domino model project: Surface area equals $56 + (1/3)\,(30 + 22 + 14 + 6) = 80$ domino squares.
Step pyramid:
1. $16{,}520$ m^2
2. 23.760 m^2
3. $40{,}280$ m^2

Aztec Area Measure

Reproducible 18

ANSWERS

Area in square quahuitls and tax in cacao beans:
   farm 1: 49, 2–3 beans
   farm 2: 420, 21 beans
   farm 3: 264, 13–14 beans
   farm 4: 94.5, 4–5 beans
   farm 5: 140, 7 beans

No, because the sum of the other two lengths is 20 quahuitls. A sum of more than 22.7 quahuitls would be needed to connect sides 17 and 15 at a right angle ($\sqrt{17^2 + 15^2} = 22.7$).

25

Volume of Pyramids

Reproducible 19

ANSWERS

Three Pyramids

1. $(26/9) (56^2 + 50^2 + 44^2 + 38^2 + 32^2 + 26^2 + 20^2 + 14^2 + 8^2) m^3 = (26/9) (3136 + 2500 + 1936 + 1444 + 1024 + 676 + 400 + 196 + 64) m^3 = 11,376 \times 26/9 \ m^3 = 32,864 \ m^3$

2. (a) $10 (16,520 + 13568 + 10904 + 8528 + 6440 + 4640) = 10 \times 60600 = 606,000 \ m^3$

   (b) More than a true pyramid, $140 \times 118 \times 60/3 = 330,400 \ m^3$

3. (a) $2,596,000 \ m^3$

   (b) $91,710,000 \ ft^3$

The Greatest Pyramid of All

Reproducible 20

ANSWERS

1. (a) $56 \ cubits^3$

   (b) $60 \ cubits^3$

   (c) Error = 4 cubits, $4/56 = 7\%$, a relatively small error

Trial length	Width = $^3/_4$ length	Product	Error = 12-product
1	$^3/_4$	$^3/_4$	$11^1/_4$
2	$^3/_2$	3	9
3	$^9/_4$	$^{27}/_4$	$5^3/_4$
4	3	12	0

Experiments with Circles and Cylinders

Reproducible 24

ANSWERS

Questions for Critical Thinking

1. $a = 1 \times h$

2. Answers will vary.

3. Answers will vary.

4. 3.16

5. 0.06%

6. (a) $640 \ cubits^3$

   (b) $384 \ cubits^3$, or 11520 hekats

The Search for π

Reproducible 25

ANSWERS

Project

Step 7: 3.11

Critical Thinking

1. Answers will vary.

2. (a) Ah'mose's method was more accurate.

   (b) Answers will vary.

3. Answers will vary.

4. Answers will vary.

5. $25.5 \ cm^2$, $31.95 \ cm^2$, $36.4 \ cm^2$, $39.38 \ cm^2$, $50.27 \ cm^2$

Circles from Mesopotamia

Reproducible 26

ANSWERS

1. 5 unit squares

2. $d = 20$. Old area = 300.
   $\pi(r + 5)^2 - \pi r^2 = 375$, $r = 10$
   Area increased 125%

Native American Circular Mounds

Reproducible 27

ANSWERS

1. Area = 81,700 m^2, Circumference = 1,013 m, Diagonal = 332.4 m

2. 1,130,000 ft^2

3. Apothem = 753 ft, Area = 1,880,000 ft^2

4. Inner square = 26 × 4840 yd^2 × 9 ft^2/yd^2 = area 1,132,560 ft^2 for a side of 1064 ft. Add 6 ft wall thicknesses for outer square. Volume = 2(11)(6)(1064) + 2(11)(6)(1078) = 282,744 ft^3. Rounded off, 280,000 ft^3.

Name _____

Date _____

Trade and the Cubit

Long before there were cities, and long before there was writing, trade routes stretched far and wide around the world. People have always been great travelers and traders. Probably then, as today, one of the first questions traders asked was, "How much?" As trade increased, measurement and arithmetic developed.

Cloth was a valuable trade item throughout the ancient world. Cloth of a standard width was sold by length. For something as valuable as fine cloth, length could not be measured by just anyone's arm-lengths. The buyer would want to use a giant's arm. The seller would want to use a baby's arm. So they agreed on a standard, the length of the Egyptian pharaoh's forearm, and called it a *cubit*. Palms and fingers were used for shorter lengths. There were 4 fingers to 1 palm, and 7 palms to 1 cubit.

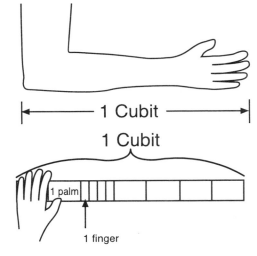

Project for Groups of 4

Find out if you have the same proportions as the pharaoh who modeled the cubit. Check off each step as you complete it. Record your results in the table below.

❑ 1. For each student, count the number of your 4-finger palms to your personal cubit. Bend your arm and count from the tip of your middle finger to the elbow joint.

❑ 2. For each student, mark your height on the wall with an erasable pencil. Then measure your height with your personal cubit and 4-finger palms. Calculate the ratio of height, column 3, to number of palms in your personal cubit, column 2.

1. Name	2. Number of palms to personal cubit	3. Height in personal cubits and palms	4. Ratio of column 3 to column 2

Discussion: Does the table show much difference among members of your group? How does your measure compare with the pharaoh's?

Geometry Activities from Many Cultures

Number Lines and the Egyptian Zero

When builders learned to work with stone in Egypt, the monuments became very heavy. Stone tombs were so heavy that they needed a deep foundation to support the weight. On the side of one of these foundations, archaeologists noticed that guidelines were still visible. When they read the numbers on the guidelines, the scientists were amazed. The numbers included a zero!

Egyptian symbol for zero, beautiful, complete.

What the archaeologists saw was actually a number line, used to position the horizontal guidelines. The guidelines were spaced evenly, 1 cubit apart. A point, perhaps at ground level, was labeled "nefer," the Egyptian word for zero. Higher points on the line were labeled "1 cubit above zero, 2 cubits above zero, 3 cubits above zero, etc." Lines below the zero level were labeled "1 cubit below zero, 2 cubits below zero, 3 cubits below zero, etc." Almost 5000 years ago, African architects were using the concept of integers, saying "above" where we say "positive" and "below" where we say "negative."

Class Project: Make an Egyptian vertical number line, using about 2 to 3 m of adding-machine tape for each student. Mark a zero reference point, perhaps desk level, and label it nefer, the Egyptian zero. Evenly spacing the numbers 1 cubit (52.5 cm) apart, label points above the zero by the number of cubits below zero. You may wish to decorate your number lines with some of the symbols you see below. Then tape all the number lines on the wall.

nefer
(zero level)

3 cubits
below zero

5 cubits
below zero

7 cubits above zero
6 cubits above zero
5 cubits above zero
4 cubits above zero
2 cubits above zero
3 cubits above zero
2 cubits above zero
1 cubit above zero
1 cubit below zero
2 cubits below zero
3 cubits below zero
4 cubits below zero
5 cubits below zero
6 cubits below zero

ground level(zero)

Geometry Activities from Many Cultures

Measures in Ancient India

In the Indus River valley, magnificent ruins remain from the ancient civilization of northwest India and Pakistan. The culture is known as Harappan, with centers at Harappa, Monhenjo-Daro, and Lothal. The Harappans left a script to describe their great deeds, but modern scholars have translated only a few words of the script.

Obviously, the Harappans were masters of geometry because their cities were well planned and their buildings were regular in form. These ancient Indians may have been the first to develop the art of fire-baked bricks, and that is only part of the story. The bricks were mass produced in precise shapes. From these bricks, and parts of measuring rulers that go back 4500 years, we can figure out the ancient Indian unit of length. The markings on the rulers are very accurate, with lines only 0.05 mm thick. Standard weights have also survived.

Harappan
stone figure

Questions for Critical Thinking

1. Standard dimensions for the bricks that line the Great Bath at Mohenjo-Daro were (300 × 150 × 75) mm. The bath was box-shaped (a rectangular prism shape) measuring 11.89 m long, 7.01 m wide, and 2.44 m deep.

   (a) How many standard bricks would it take to go around the perimeter of the bath with one course of bricks?

   (b) How many standard bricks would it take to line the bath? *Hint:* Draw a diagram. Round off to the next higher integer.

2. Scientists are studying buildings that may have been warehouses at the ancient Indian cities of Harappa and Mohenjo-Daro. The scientists hope that geometry can provide information about the functions of these buildings. They measured the area of the structures and compared them to the size of the town, as shown below in the following table.

	Size of town in hectares	Area of building in m²	Floor space in m²
Harappa	100	2104	984
Lothal	10	2005	832
Mohenjo-Daro	125	1650	749

   (a) Is the area of the building proportional to the size of the town? Show your calculations.

   (b) What are the ratios of the area of the buildings to the floor space?

   (c) If these buildings were warehouses, do you think they served the town or larger regions? Why do you think so?

Geometry Activities from Many Cultures

Geometry for City Planning

TEOTIHUACÁN: GRANDER THAN ROME

The ancient city of Teotihuacán

Situated in the Valley of Mexico, the city of Teotihuacán was one of the largest cities in the world during its high period from 100 B.C.E. to 750 C.E. It was larger and grander than Rome at the height of the Roman Empire, and certainly cleaner. A drainage system and regular removal of waste materials safeguarded the city's sanitation. The population has been estimated at 100,000. Imagine the dramatic sight as visitors entered the city. The six-tiered Pyramid of the Sun dominated the scene, with carved serpent heads protruding from brightly painted walls. At the other end of the wide avenue rose the Pyramid of the Moon, also ablaze with color.

Perhaps the most impressive feature of Teotihuacán was the geometric city plan. The city was arranged on a rectangular grid that ran for miles, through the city and up into the hills. Even the river that ran through the city was altered to make its course follow the plan of the grid. The Street of the Dead, the north-south axis, and the east-west axis, now called East Avenue and West Avenue, divide the city in quadrants. The layout is similar to Chicago's State Street and Madison Street.

Individual squares of the grid measured about 57 m. Cut into some floors and rocks, there are two concentric circles and a cross that divides the circle into quadrants. Many scientists believe these symbols were used for astronomy and to regulate the calendar. A pair of these designs, two miles apart, determines a line exactly perpendicular to the Street of the Dead, the north-south axis of Teotihuacán. These markers are aligned with the setting point of the Pleiades stars, the stars in Orion's belt. Apparently, the basic plan of Teotihuacán was determined by astronomy.

(continued)

Geometry for City Planning *(continued)*

Who lived in Teotihuacán? Certainly priests, government officials, merchants, and craftspeople. But none of these people produced food. It is believed that many farmers also lived in the city and went out each day to work their fields. The type of farming was intensive and productive and still goes on today. They farmed *chinampas,* islands of earth that float in shallow lakes.

Housing was part of the city plan and allowed a high population density while preserving privacy. There were about 4000 one-story apartment buildings. Each had a solid wall to the exterior. Inside there were open, sunlit patio areas. Apartments had access to a private or semiprivate patio but were shielded from the noise of the street. Modern visitors to Teotihuacán may find the residential streets dull, because all that can be seen are the solid exterior walls. The family life was private, centered on the inside courtyards. Some apartment buildings belonged to extended families, but others were centers for specialized crafts. Each patio in every apartment building had its own drainage and sanitation system.

After 850 years, Teotihuacán burned down. Hundreds of years later, the city's glory was reborn in the Aztec capital of Tenochtitlán. Today, Mexico City stands on the stones of Tenochtitlán.

Questions for Critical Thinking

1. What are some of the advantages of building a city from a plan?

2. What are some possible disadvantages of making the plan first and then building the city?

3. What mathematical tools do you think the Mexicans needed to build Teotihuacán on a rectangular grid?

4. Why do you think the early Mexicans studied astronomy?

5. Suppose you were a historian, trying to find out why Teotihuacán lost power after 850 years. What possible causes would you investigate?

Geometry Activities from Many Cultures

The Nile Floods and the Birth of Geometry

Early civilization in Egypt and the Sudan depended on agriculture, and agriculture depended on the Nile River. Every year at the end of August, the Nile would swell to twice its normal size and turn into a roaring flood. Low-lying land near the river remained flooded for weeks. People welcomed the flood because the river brought water for their crops. When the river went down, it left a rich silt that fertilized the fields. Rain was rare. It was neither expected nor welcome.

In theory, all the land in Egypt belonged to the king, or pharaoh, who held it for the people of Egypt. In practice, much of the land had been divided into farms that families held for generations. The farmers' first task, after the river went down, was to plant the seed. But all of the boundaries had been washed away. How did they decide whose land was whose?

The traditional belief was that Egyptians invented geometry to restore farm boundaries each year. Whatever the reason, in ancient times Egypt was the place to study geometry. The earliest Greek mathematicians went to Egypt to study, perhaps to get the ancient form of a Ph.D., the doctor of philosophy degree. When the Greek students returned home, they brought Egyptian mathematics, science, and culture with them.

In most cases it was not hard to measure the area of farms. Egyptians had already developed their unit of length, the cubit. The cubit was fixed as the length of the forearm of an early pharaoh, equivalent to 52.5 cm. To measure area, the square of 1 cubit × 1 cubit was standard. Today we can use our modern shorthand to write this as 1 cubit^2. To find the area of a figure, Egyptians counted the number of 1 cubit × 1 cubit squares that fit into the figure. In time they found shortcuts, the same formulas that we use today.

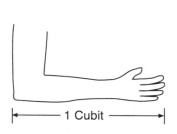

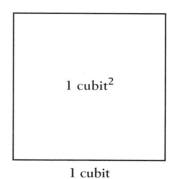

1 cubit^2

1 cubit

AREA EXAMPLES FROM THE AH'MOSE PAPYRUS

Over 4000 years ago, ancient Egyptians had discovered most of the formulas for area and volume that we use today. Some of these early formulas were:

Area of a rectangle = lw (length × width)

Area of a triangle = $\frac{1}{2} bh$ (base × height)

Area of a trapezoid = $\frac{1}{2} h(b_1 + b_2)$

(continued)

Geometry Activities from Many Cultures

The Nile Floods and the Birth of Geometry *(continued)*

Area Examples from the Ah'mose Papyrus

These formulas are used in one of the few surviving mathematical books from Egypt. It was copied by the scribe Ah'mose from a book written in 1850 B.C.E. The numbering here comes from the translation of Ah'mose's papyrus called the *Rhind Mathematical Papyrus.* Rhind bought the papyrus book in Egypt in 1858.

Solve the following examples from Ah'mose's book. Work with a partner on examples 2 and 3.

1. Ah'mose Example 49, with a copy of his diagram:

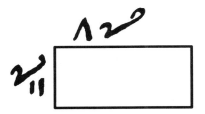

after Chace, 1927–29

   What is the area of a rectangle of land of 10 khet by 1 khet? Note that 1 khet = 100 cubits.

   (a) Draw a diagram of the rectangle.

   (b) Find the area in cubits². Area = _____ cubits².

   (c) Find the area in m². Use 1 cubit = 0.525 m. Area = _____ m².

2. Ah'mose example 51: Example of a triangle of land. Suppose it is said to thee, What is the area of a triangle of side 10 khet and altitude of 4 khet? (Use 1 khet = 100 cubits.)

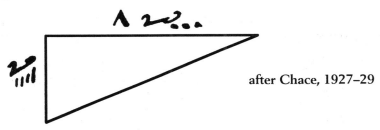

after Chace, 1927–29

   The Ah'mose solution says, "Take ½ of 4 in order to get its rectangle. Multiply 10 times 2; this is its area." Notice that area is in khet².

   (a) Draw a diagram of the triangle.

   (b) Find the area in cubits². _____

   (c) What formula for area was Ah'mose using?

   (d) What do you think Ah'mose meant when he said take half the base "in order to get the rectangle." Experiment by making two copies of your diagram. Cut them out. Can you arrange them to "get the rectangle?"

   (continued)

Geometry Activities from Many Cultures

More Area Examples
from the Ah'mose Papyrus

Here are some more area examples from the Ah-mose Papyrus.

1. Ah'mose example 52: What is the area of a trapezoidal section of land with altitude 20 khet, and bases 6 khet and 4 khet? (Use 1 khet = 100 cubits.)

   Ah'mose's solution: Add the bases. Then take $\frac{1}{2}$ of the sum "in order to get its rectangle." Multiply by 20.

   (a) Draw a diagram of the trapezoid and find the area in cubits^2.

   (b) What formula for area was Ah'mose using?

   (c) Ah'mose said take $\frac{1}{2}$ the sum of the bases "in order to get the rectangle." What did he mean? Experiment by cutting out two copies of the diagram of the trapezoid and rearranging the parts to "get the rectangle."

2. Area problems in the Moscow Mathematical Papyrus: The scribe who wrote the Moscow mathematical papyrus solved an area problem by using an equation and finding a square root. You can try an experimental approach by completing the table below.

   Find the length and width. A rectangle of area 12 had a width that is $\frac{3}{4}$ the length.

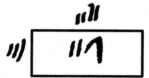

Area of rectangle
equals 12 square units.

Problem 6, Moscow Mathematical Papyrus

	Trial length	Width = $\frac{3}{4}$ length	Product = LW	Error = 12 − product
1				
2				
3				
4				
5				

The correct length is _____ cubits. The width is _____ cubits.

Geometry Activities from Many Cultures

Surface Area of a Step Pyramid

Step pyramid

In Africa and Central America, huge pyramids were built to show the power and glory of those civilizations. To build these pyramids, the ancient engineers had to solve some of the same geometry problems that we study today.

The first stone pyramid of Africa was a step pyramid, not a true pyramid shape. It consisted of six rectangular layers, each one set back from the lower layer. The architect was the multigenius Imhotep, also revered as the founder of the science of medicine. To make the pyramid even more beautiful, the exposed surfaces were covered with gleaming white limestone. To find the amount of limestone needed, Egyptian architects had to calculate the surface area of the pyramid.

Supposing that the pyramid is 140 m by 118 m at the base, the height is 60 m, and each of the six steps are set back 6 m from each side, what is its surface area? For simplicity, assume that each step was of equal height. An exploration with a small model pyramid can help us find the surface area of the Saqqara pyramid.

Project

MATERIALS

> 50 dominoes
> double-sided tape

With 50 dominoes and a little tape, you can model a four-level step pyramid. It should be easy to count the squares, two to each domino, and find the surface area of a domino pyramid. The height of a domino varies with the brand. We'll assume the height is $\frac{1}{3}$ of a domino square.

(continued)

Surface Area of a Step Pyramid *(continued)*

Check off each step as you complete it.

❑ 1. Arrange the dominoes as follows:

Bottom layer: A rectangle of 28 dominoes, with 4 double-lengths the long way, 7 domino widths on the short side. This makes a total of 56 squares. Use two-sided tape to keep the layers together.

Second layer: 15 dominoes arranged with 3 double-lengths the long way, 5 domino widths on the short side.

Third layer: 6 dominoes, with 2 double-lengths the long way, 3 domino widths on the short side.

Top layer: 1 domino.

❑ 2. Calculate the surface area of the domino pyramid. The answer can be given in domino square units.

Hint: Surface area consists of exposed tops and sides. Look down at the model pyramid, from a point directly above the pyramid. From this viewpoint, the sum of the exposed tops equals the area of the base. The sides are easily calculated from the perimeter of each layer. Assume the height of each layer is $\frac{1}{3}$ the length of the domino square. There are two squares to each domino.

A DAZZLING WHITE STEP PYRAMID

Imhotep, designer of the first pyramid at Saqqara, needed to know how much fine limestone was needed to cover the six-step pyramid. Our exploration with the four-step pyramid modeled with dominoes showed us the key to this puzzle. Divide the surfaces into horizontal and vertical surfaces. The sum of the areas of the horizontal surfaces of the pyramid is equal to the area of the pyramid's base. Add the area of the sides to the area of the base of the pyramid to find the area of all the pyramid surfaces.

White step pyramid

The base of the pyramid measures 140 m × 118 m. The area of the sides for each layer is equal to the perimeter times the height of the step. Since there are six steps and the pyramid height is 60 m, we can take the height of each step as approximately 10 m. To find the perimeter of the layers, we must subtract the amount that each side is set back. Suppose each layer is set back 6 m on each side. The perimeter of each layer would be 48 m less than the layer just below it.

Calculate and fill in the following.

    1. Base area = _____

    2. Area of sides of layers = _____

    3. Exposed surface area of pyramid is _____

Name _____

Date _____

Aztec Area Measure

The Nahua (Nahuatl) language, spoken by the Aztec of Mexico, had many words for counting and for tools used for geometry. These words include:

compass, *tlayolloanaloni*   square, *tlanacazamimi*

plumb line, *temetzetepilolli*   level, *quamniztli*

Great Aztec cities, temples, and pyramids still stand as proof of the geometric ability of their builders. However, knowledge of the Aztec surveying methods had been lost over the centuries since the Spanish Conquest. It was only in recent years that modern mathematicians learned about the Aztec numerals that use positional value and a zero symbol. The burning of Native American books by the Spanish conquerors in the 1500's destroyed most of the Aztec records. Fortunately, an Aztec tax record escaped the fires of the Inquisition and was recently found near Texcoco, Mexico.

The Texcoco record shows that Aztec measurements of area were more accurate than the old Spanish measurements for the same farm plots. In the 1500's, Spanish mathematicians were among the finest of Europe. If Aztec area measurement was better than the Spanish, it says a lot for the level of Aztec technology. Another factor in accurate measurement was the reliable Aztec unit of length, called the *quahuitl*. In contrast, the Spanish unit of length, the *vara*, was often changed for reasons of greed or politics. The quahuitl measures about 2.5 m or 3 Spanish varas in length.

Project

The areas of farms were carefully calculated by Aztec surveyors for tax purposes. The following list has just a few of the 1100 entries on the original Texcoco record. The lengths of all sides are given for these farm plots. Since the terrain near Texcoco is hilly and rugged, most farms were not rectangular. The tax rate was 1 cacao bean for 20 square quahuitls. You can estimate the tax in cacao beans for the farms listed on the next page. Here is an example.

Example: On graph paper, make a diagram of an Aztec farm plot whose sides measure 10, 14, 9, and 13 quahuitls. Connect the 14 and 10 quahuitl sides at a right angle. The area is 127 square quahuitls; the tax is 7 cacao beans.

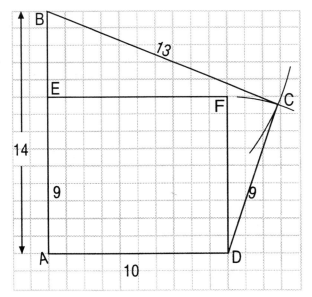

Geometry Activities from Many Cultures

Aztec Area Measure *(continued)*

TEXCOCO AZTEC LAND RECORDS

Lengths in quahuitls for sides of farm plots in Texcoco, Mexico:

Farm 1: 17, 15, 11, 9

Farm 2: 20, 20, 20, 22

Farm 3: 15, 18, 16, 17

Farm 4: 7, 13, 33, 14

Farm 5: 14, 10, 14, 10

A Project

Make scale drawings to outline the Texcoco farms with lengths given.

Check off each step as you complete it.

❑   1.   Use graph paper, a compass, and a straightedge to draw these quadrilaterals to scale, using the dimensions listed. If possible, connect two sides at right angles.

❑   2.   Divide the area of each quadrilateral into rectangles and right triangles. Find the approximate areas.

❑   3.   Find the tax in cacao beans for each.

Question for Critical Thinking

For the plot with 17, 15, 11, and 9 quahuitls, can the side that is 17 quahuitls long meet the side that's 15 quahuitls long at a right angle? Why or why not? (Hint: Draw a diagram and calculate the length of the longer diagonal of the quadrilateral.)

Name _____

Date _____

Volume of Pyramids

Group Project

The architects of the pyramids had very practical reasons for calculating the volume of the pyramid they were planning. To calculate the number of workers that would be needed, they asked, "How much stone will it take to fill the pyramid?" Pyramids were built in solid form. A stone core was used in the African pyramids. In contrast, the interior of Central American pyramids contained blocks of a type of concrete invented by the early Americans.

For step pyramids, the formula for volume, $v = lwh$, could be used to find the volume of each step. Then the volumes could be added. But the true pyramid shape was a challenge. Some believe that Egyptian mathematicians found the volume of a square pyramid by comparing it to a square prism of the same base and height. The volume of a square pyramid is:

$v = (\frac{1}{3})a^2h$, where a = length of the side of the base, h = height.

You can verify this formula by making models of a pyramid and a prism.

Check off each step as you complete it.

❑ 1. Enlarge these patterns for a pyramid and a prism of the same base and height.

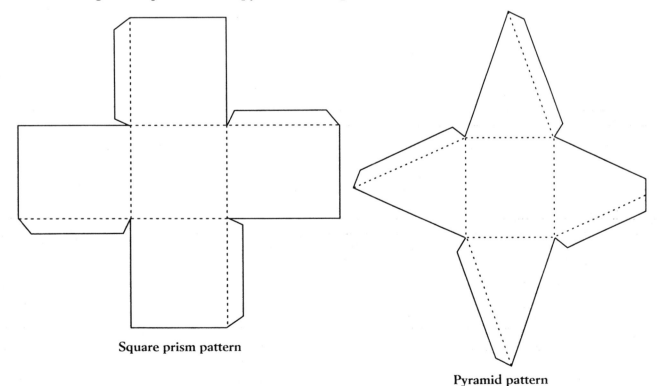

Square prism pattern

Pyramid pattern

(continued)

Geometry Activities from Many Cultures

Volume of Pyramids *(continued)*

❑ 2. Cut out the patterns. Fold on the dotted lines and tape in place with plenty of tape. With small scissors, remove the base of the pyramid so it can be filled with oatmeal or rice.

❑ 3. Fill the pyramid with dry oatmeal or rice. Level off the top. Pour into the prism.

❑ 4. Repeat until the prism is just full. If you are careful, that will be an exact number of times.

Group Discussion

1. What is the formula for the volume of a square prism with base sides *a* and height *h*?

2. How many full pyramids did it take to fill the prism?

3. What is the formula for the volume of the pyramid?

THREE PYRAMIDS

Find the volume of three of the most famous pyramids in the world. For the step pyramids, assume that the height of each step is the same and that the volume of each layer equals *lwh*.

1. The Toltec-Maya pyramid of Kukulkán, popularly known as the Castillo, measures about 56 m on each side of the base. This step pyramid rises 26 m in 9 layers. Each succeeding layer is set back 3 m on each side. There is a temple on the flat top.

    What is the approximate volume of the pyramid, not counting the temple? *Hint:* There are only 8 setbacks for 9 layers. Find the sum of the volumes of each layer.

2. The 6-step pyramid at Saqqara had a rectangular base of 140 m by 118 m. The height was 60 m. Each of the 6 layers, or steps, were set back 6 m from each side.

    (a) Find the volume.

    (b) Without calculating, do you think this is more or less than a true pyramid of the same **height and base**? Calculate and check your guess.

3. Khufu's Pyramid, also known as the Great Pyramid, has a true pyramid shape. The original height was about 481.4 ft, or 146.7 m. Each side of the square base is about 756 ft, or 230.4 m.

    (a) Calculate the volume in m^3. (Round off your answers to four significant figures.)

    (b) Calculate the volume in ft^3. (Round off your answers to four significant figures.)

Geometry Activities from Many Cultures

The Greatest Pyramid of All

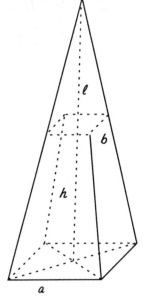

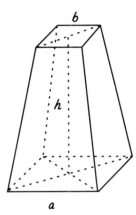

Ancient Egyptian mathematicians made an amazing discovery! They correctly developed the advanced formula for the volume of a truncated pyramid. The formula was

$$v = (1/3)(h)(a^2 + ab + b^2).$$

This complex formula, at least 3800 years old, gives the volume of the truncated (shortened) pyramid shown above. Here h is the height, a^2 is the area of the base, and b^2 is the area of the flat top.

This formula has been called the greatest pyramid of all. Nobody knows how the Egyptians made the discovery. Some believe it was done by a combination of algebra and geometry. Perhaps you, or someone in your class, will solve the mystery one day. Historians assume that Egyptians knew the basic pyramid formula, $v = (1/3)a^2h$. If they subtracted the pyramid cut off from the original pyramid, they would have:

$v = (1/3)a^2(h + l) - (1/3)b^2l$. After some further steps:

$v = (1/3)(h)(a^2 + ab + b^2)$.

Questions for Critical Thinking

1. For a truncated pyramid with $a = 4$ cubits, $b = 2$ cubits, and $h = 6$ cubits:

   (a) Use the correct Egyptian formula for volume, $v = (1/3)(h)(a^2 + ab + b^2)$.

   (b) Use an incorrect Babylonian formula for volume, $v = (1/2)(h)(a^2 + b^2)$.

   (c) Is the error that resulted from using the Babylonian formula small or large?

   (d) Do you think the Egyptians could have found their formula by trial and error?

Name _____

Date _____

The Circle as Perfection

The idea of the circle as perfection is widespread in many cultures. In *Africa Counts*, the author shows the space-saving advantages of a round house. She quotes an African poet, Joseph Waiguru, who praises the traditional round house of Kenya:

The round warm hut

Proud to the last

Of her noble sons

And daughters . . .

Round House, Tanzania

In *Black Elk Speaks*, the leader of the Oglala Sioux speaks about the cultural value of circles:

"You have noticed that everything an Indian does is in a circle, and that is because the Power of the World always works in circles, and everything tries to be round."

The Greeks and Egyptians 2000 years ago thought that planets and stars orbited in circles, because anything less would not be perfect. Now we know that the planets travel in elliptical orbits, and that is fine with modern scientists. But circles still play a vital role in science. The mathematics of circles is used to model cyclical events, such as alternating current in electricity. Circles remain a favorite form for art and design.

Group Discussion

1. List five or more popular expressions that use "circle."

2. Cities and towns have few circular buildings. Why do you think this is so?

3. Cities like Paris and Washington, D.C., are built on a circular grid rather than a rectangular grid. What are some possible advantages or disadvantages for the circular and for the rectangular city grids?

4. What types of symmetry can you find in the circle? Is there any type of symmetry of design that a circle does not have?

5. On separate sheets of paper, use your compass to make two designs featuring circles.

   (a) Use concentric circles.

   (b) Use intersecting circles

Geometry Activities from Many Cultures

Name _____

Date _____

Circles in Kenya and Mexico

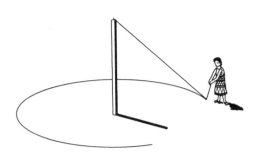

The Gikuyu people who live on the slopes of Mount Kenya built their round houses from the wood of cedar trees. Construction of the house began with a perfect circle drawn on the ground. The beauty of the house depended on this first step. Then holes were dug, evenly spaced around the circle, for the foundation posts.

How did the Gikuyu draw their foundation circles? Everyone who has drawn a circle with a compass has an instinctive "feel" for the geometry of a circle. All points on the circumference must be equidistant from the center. In the Gikuyu "compass," the fixed arm was a pole with a strong cord tied to the top. A marker was attached to the free end of the cord. The moving arm of the compass was a person walking around the pole, pulling the cord and using the marker to draw a circle on the ground.

Project

Make your own compass from materials in your home or classroom. Show your class how you can draw circles with your homemade compass.

CIRCLES IN AZTEC THOUGHT

Aztec Calendar Stone

A famous stone sculpture, 3.6 m (12 ft) in diameter and weighing 24 metric tons, is the centerpiece of Mexico's Museum of Anthropology. Eight concentric circles on the face of the stone disc contain figures and writing that tells the story of the Aztec people. The sun at the center is called the Fifth Sun because four earlier suns were destroyed by jaguars, wind, fiery rain, and water. Sometimes the stone is called the Calendar Stone because one of the circular bands gives the 20-day names of the 260-day sacred calendar.

The Aztecs needed to know a lot about the geometry of the circle to design this stone. How did they divide the circles so accurately to give equal placement for the 20 day names? We do know that they used a compass, called *tlayolloanaloni*.

Project

Read about the Stone of the Fifth Sun in the *National Geographic*, December 1980, 758 ff. Then design your own concentric-circle picture in which you tell part of the story of the Aztecs or any other people.

Geometry Activities from Many Cultures

Name _____

Date _____

Circles in Egypt

Some of the Egyptian farms near the Nile River were in the shape of a semicircle. Farmers needed to know the area of these farms. That was a great challenge for mathematicians 4000 years ago. They knew how to multiply cubits by cubits to get units of area. Cubits[3] gave them units of volume. But when it came to curves, they had trouble measuring with a straight-line tool like the cubit stick.

Try to count the square units in the following figures. You will quickly see the challenge of measuring the area of a curved figure with square units. Do you see why finding the area of a circle was called squaring the circle?

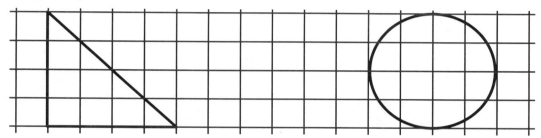

Egyptians found a very good formula for the area of a circle 3,650 years ago. The scribe Ah'mose showed the method:

Take a square whose side is $\frac{8}{9}$ the diameter of the circle. The area of that square equals the area of the circle.

We can write this formula in modern terms as: Area = $[(\frac{8}{9})\,D]^2$.

Test this formula on the example that Ah'mose gave for a circle whose diameter is 9 cubits. The Egyptian formula for area gives $(\frac{8}{9}$ of $9)^2$, or 64 cubits. Check this answer with the modern formula of $A = \pi r^2$. We get $\pi(4.5)^2 = 63.62$ cubits, very close to 64 cubits. The percent error is only 0.6%.

The picture Ah'mose supplied in his problem is shown here. It gives us the clue to his method. He shows a square, 9 cubits × 9 cubits and trisects the sides. Connecting trisection points gives him an octagon. He could easily see that a circle of diameter 9 has almost the same area as the octagon. So Ah'mose looked for a square whose area was very close to the area of the octagon. The square he found had sides equal to $\frac{8}{9}$ the diameter of the circle.

**Egyptian script reads 9 cubits.
That is the length of the side.
after Chace, 1927–29**

Geometry Activities from Many Cultures

Circles in Egypt *(continued)*

DISCOVER A FORMULA FOR THE AREA OF A CIRCLE

Project

You can follow in Ah'mose's footsteps and model his discovery method.

Check off each step as you complete it.

❑   1. On 1-cm grid paper, outline two squares, each containing 9×9 1-cm square units. Each square unit will stand for 1 cubit². Set one 9×9 square aside for later use.

❑   2. Inside one 9×9 square, inscribe a circle of diameter 9 (radius $4\frac{1}{2}$) with center at the center of the square.

❑   3. Connect trisection points on adjacent sides to outline an octagon. Observe that the area of the octagon is almost equal to the area of the circle. (Trisection points on each side of the square are 3 units from the nearest corner.)

❑   4. Shade in the 4 corners cut out of the square by the octagon. With scissors, cut off and save the 4 shaded corners, as shown in Figure 2. The total of square units cut out is 18. They represent the difference between the area of the 9×9 square and the octagon.

❑   5. Cut apart the 4 corners to make two rows of square units, each row 1-unit high. You will need to tape triangles together to form squares. Arrange the pieces to cover the top row and the first column on the left of the remaining 9×9 square you made in step 1. They should fit exactly, with one square left over as shown in Figure 3. The part of the 9×9 square that remains uncovered is an 8×8 square. This uncovered area almost equals the area of the octagon, and therefore the circle. The error is the one square left over, or 1 part in 63.

Hint: Placing some paste or stick glue on the left column and top row of the square will make it easier to keep the small pieces of paper in place.

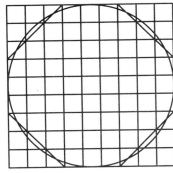

Figure 1

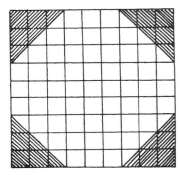

Figure 2

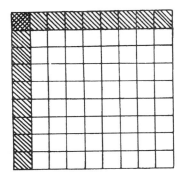

Figure 3
after Gillings, 1972

(continued)

Geometry Activities from Many Cultures

Name _____

Date _____

Experiments with Circles and Cylinders

Egyptians discovered much of their geometry by comparing figures, looking for figures with equal areas, or similar shapes, or both. You can explore geometry by examining and comparing some common objects.

Class Project

MATERIALS

> string, meterstick or tailor's tape
> circular objects such as round-topped bowls and wastebaskets
> 1 inner cardboard tube from a toilet paper roll

Check off each step as you complete it.

❑ 1. Stand the tube on end. Measure the height and the diameter of the tube. Record the diameter in the table below. You will need the height for step 5.

❑ 2. Gently tear or cut open the tube along its seam and unroll it to a flat shape. The shape is a _____.

❑ 3. Measure the edge that formed the circumference of the tube. Record your reading below.

❑ 4. Cut along the shorter diagonal of the unrolled tube. The length of this diagonal is equal to the height of the original tube.

❑ 5. Reassemble the two pieces to form a rectangle. Ancient Egyptians called this, "getting the rectangle." Calculate the area of the rectangle. The area = _____.

❑ 6. With a string and meterstick, or a tailor's tape, measure the diameter and circumference of the rim to two bowls and a round basket. Record your results in the following table.

❑ 7. Calculate the ratio of C/D, circumference divided by the diameter.

Item	Circumference	Diameter	Ratio of C/d
toilet paper tube	_____	_____	_____
rim of bowl 1	_____	_____	_____
rim of bowl 2	_____	_____	_____
rim of basket	_____	_____	_____

❑ 8. Average the class or group's values for C/D.

(continued)

© 1997 Beatrice Lumpkin
J. Weston Walch, Publisher

Geometry Activities from Many Cultures

Experiments with Circles and Cylinders (continued)

Questions for Critical Thinking

1. The unrolled cylindrical paper tube had the shape of a parallelogram. To find the area of the parallelogram, you cut it apart and reassembled the pieces to make a rectangle of equal area. From this experiment, you can state the formula for the area of a parallelogram in terms of its height and the length of its base.

   Area of parallelogram = _____.

2. A rectangle can be rolled around and taped to form a cylinder. Why do you suppose the toilet paper manufacturers made the tube from a parallelogram instead of from a rectangle?

3. The Greek letter π stands for a constant, the ratio of the circumference of a circle divided by its diameter. How close was your experimental value to $\pi = 3.14$, correct to 3 significant figures? How close was the class or group average? What was the percent error of the class average, compared to the value $\pi = 3.14$?

4. Compare the ancient Egyptian formula for the area of a circle, $A = [(^8\!/_9)D]^2$, with the modern formula, πr^2. Substitute $D = 2r$ in the Egyptian formula to find the Egyptian equivalent of π.

5. What was the percent error in the Egyptian value for π that you found?

6. For the volume of a cylinder, the scribe Ah'mose used $v = [(^8\!/_9)D]^2 l$, with l = length of the cylinder. Use this formula to solve the next two problems from the Ah'mose papyrus.

   (a) Ah'mose problem 41. Find the volume of a cylindrical granary of diameter 9 cubits and height 10 cubits.

   (b) Ah'mose problem 43. A cylindrical granary has a diameter of 9 cubits and a height of 6 cubits. What is the amount of grain that goes into it, measured in hekats? Use the conversion factor, 1 cubit^3 = 30 hekats of grain.

The Search for π

What is the value of π, the constant ratio of the circumference of any circle divided by its diameter? This question has fascinated and entertained people who work with numbers for many years,. Everyone who has measured circles, starting with the ancient Egyptians and Babylonians, had to use π. Engineers and scientists concerned with wheels and repeating cycles of change need accurate values for π.

Of course, the ancient mathematicians never spoke about "π." That is a Greek letter and Greeks did not have an alphabet 4,000 years ago. But Egyptians and Babylonians did have a written language and were measuring circles that long ago. You can find the ancient equivalents for π. Just match the modern formula πr^2 with the ancient formulas for the area of a circle.

Some Values for π through History

Year (approximate)	Source	Approximation to π
1850 B.C.E.	Ahmose, Egypt	3.16
1800 B.C.E.	Old Babylonian tablets	Many tablets use 3. Susa tablet uses 3.125
965 B.C.E.	Old Testament 1 Kings 7:23	3
500 B.C.E.	Sulbasutras from India	3.09
240 B.C.E.	Archimedes, Greece	3.14
150	Ptolemy, Egypt	3.14167
260	Liu Hui, China	3.1416
500	Aryabhata, India	3.1416
1400	Mahdava, India	3.14159265359
1429	Al-Kashi, Central Asia	3.1415926535897932
1946	Ferguson, England	correct to 710 places
1989	Chudnovsky, U.S.A. (with computer)	to 1,011,196,691 places

(continued)

Geometry Activities from Many Cultures

The Search for π *(continued)*

OLD BABYLONIAN FORMULA FOR THE AREA OF A CIRCLE

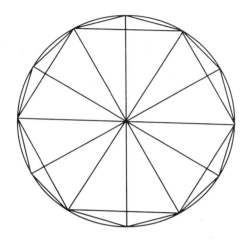

In Old Babylonia, about 1800 B.C.E., mathematical problems were written on clay tablets. Most of the tablets with problems about circles had values equivalent to $\pi = 3$. However, a Babylonian tablet from Susa has a better value, $\pi = 3.125$. It is believed that Babylonians found these values by comparing the circumference of a circle to the perimeter of the hexagon inscribed in the circle. Your group can find your own experimental values for π and check a method that may have been used in Babylonia.

MATERIALS

compass, thread, measuring tape with centimeters

Check off each step as you complete it.

❑ 1. Use your compass to draw a circle of 6 cm radius. With your scale, measure and record the length of the diameter.

❑ 2. Form the string smoothly around this circle, using tape to keep the string in place. Mark the string, unroll, and measure the length you used around the circle.

❑ 3. Divide the circumference you just measured by the diameter and record the ratio. This is your group's personal discovery of the value for π.

❑ 4. Inscribe a hexagon in the circle as follows: Open your compass 6 cm and mark off six consecutive arcs on the circle. Connect the end points of these arcs with 6 line segments.

❑ 5. Divide the perimeter of the hexagon you drew, 6×6 cm = 36 cm, by the diameter of the circle, 12 cm. This value is the Babylonian's first approximation of π. Compare it to the value you found in step 3. Which is closer to the correct value of $\pi \approx 3.14$?

❑ 6. Inscribe a dodecagon, a 12-sided polygon inside the same circle as the hexagon you drew. To find the vertices of the dodecagon, bisect the arcs for the hexagon. Connect these midpoints to the vertices of the hexagon to form a regular dodecagon.

❑ 7. Calculate the perimeter of the dodecagon. Divide by the diameter, 12 cm, to get a better value for π. Babylonians may have used this method.

DISCOVERING VALUES FOR π

Questions for Critical Thinking

1. Why is it important to find accurate values for π (the ratio of the circumference of a circle to its diameter)?

Geometry Activities from Many Cultures

The Search for π *(continued)*

2. Mathematicians have used polygons inscribed in circles to find values close to the size of the circle. For example, Ah'mose in Egypt probably used an inscribed octagon to get π = 3.16. The Babylonians may have used an inscribed hexagon to get π = 3.

   (a) Which approximation was the most accurate?

   (b) Suggest an improvement over the Ah'mose method that would give a value closer to the real size of the circle.

3. Give two examples of when an approximate value is sufficient for the purpose.

4. Give two examples when as much accuracy as possible is needed, where even a small error can have a serious effect.

5. A circle of radius 4 cm has a circumference of about 25.1 cm. Calculate the areas of these figures which all have a perimeter of 25.1 cm.. Which provides maximum area?

   Rectangle, sides 10 cm × 2.55 cm   Area = _____

   Rectangle, sides 9 cm × 3.55 cm   Area = _____

   Rectangle, sides 8 cm × 4.55 cm   Area = _____

   Square, sides 6.275 cm   Area = _____

   Circle, radius 4 cm   Area = _____

Name _____

Date _____

Circles from Mesopotamia

The country now called Iraq was once known as Mesopotamia, the Greek name for "land between the rivers." That land, between the Tigris and Euphrates Rivers, was an ancient cradle of civilization and the sciences. Babylon was one of their great capitals. They studied geometry to help them design irrigation canals and install drainage pipes.

1. Some Babylonian geometry problems produced beautiful designs. The following problem was written in cuneiform marks (pronounced koo-nay-yi-form) pressed into clay tablets. Circles, semicircles, and quarter circles were drawn as shown below. The side of the square is 4 cubits. Find the area of the 5 shaded figures. Use $\pi = 3$.

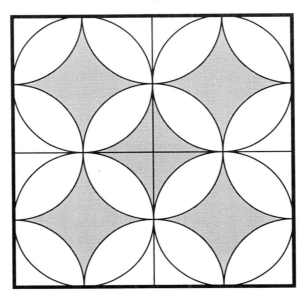

after H.W.F. Saggs, 1962

The area shaded area equals_____ cubits^2.

2. Solve this Babylonian problem:

A circular town needs more room. The boundary is extended 5 units of length, giving the town an additional area of 375 square units. What was the diameter of the old town? What was the percentage increase of area? Use $\pi = 3$.

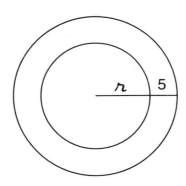

Geometry Activities from Many Cultures

Native American Circular Mounds

Spectacular feats of engineering were accomplished by a number of Native American nations who built great ceremonial centers, some as early as the year 700 C.E. Often, a temple was placed on top of a huge mound. Some mounds were circular, rectangular, octagonal, or pyramid-shaped. Other mounds were built in the shapes of birds, snakes, or other animals. The animal-shaped mounds cover so much ground that they were rediscovered only by aerial surveys.

The construction of massive monuments in special shapes required a knowledge of geometry, planning, and other engineering skills. The architects had to calculate how much earth had to be dug, how to carry it to the mound site, and how to build the stable shapes that have remained standing for up to 1000 years. Such massive construction would have required the labor of many hundreds of people over a long period of time. Meanwhile the workers had to be fed, housed, clothed, and their families maintained.

Embossed copper, Georgia

Most of the mound-building cultures were in fertile river valleys, especially the Mississippi and the Ohio Rivers. These Native American economies were rich enough to have surplus food to feed the large number of workers at the ceremonial centers. The mound builders' wealth was based on agriculture, fishing, hunting, and trade. Beyond the geometry of the mounds, which speak for themselves, we know little about their science and mathematics.

Skilled craftspeople produced fine works of art, such as the embossed copper object above. When the first Europeans came to Florida, they met people they called Natchez whose social structure was probably inherited from the mound builders. The Cherokees, Creeks and other Indian peoples are probably descendants of these advanced societies.

(continued)

Geometry Activities from Many Cultures

Name _____

Date _____

Native American Circular Mounds *(continued)*

GEOMETRY OF THE GREAT AMERICAN MOUNDS

We can understand the grand scale of Native American construction by calculating some of the areas covered by the mounds and the volume of earth and stone that were needed to build them. Here are some examples that you can explore. In each case, first draw a diagram. Then do the calculations. Give your answers rounded off to the number of significant figures used in the original measurements.

1. In a place now called High Banks, Ohio, Native Americans built an almost perfect circular mound. A square of 228 meters on each side can be inscribed inside the circular base. What is the area of ground covered by the circular mound? What is the circumference of the base of the circular mound? Give answers to three significant digits. *Hint:* Use the right-triangle theorem to find the diagonal of the square.

2. When the town of Circleville, Ohio, was founded almost 200 years ago, the town line followed the curve of a huge Native American circular embankment. The structure had been built by an Indian nation of mound builders. If the diameter of the circle measured 1200 feet, what was the original area of the town?

3. Newark, Ohio, still has traces of massive works built by the Native American people of the Hopewell culture. Remains of a regular octagon with sides 625 ft long, and diameter 1630 ft are still visible. What was the area enclosed by the octagon? *Hint:* Area = $\frac{1}{2} ap$, where a is the apothem, the distance from the center of the octagon to the midpoint of a side, and p is the perimeter. Then $a = \sqrt{[(815)^2 - (312.5)^2]}$

4. Part of the Native American earthworks built by the Hopewell people in Newark, Ohio, has walls surrounding a square area of 26 acres. If the wall was 6 ft thick and averaged 11 ft in height, what volume of earth was needed to build the wall? *Hint:* Draw a diagram allowing for the thickness of the wall. Use 1 acre = 4,840 yd^2.

Geometry Activities from Many Cultures

Similarity

Measuring the Earth's Circumference

Reproducible 28

ANSWERS

1. (a) 39,375 km, 24,471 miles
   (b) 7790 miles, close to the 7900 miles accepted today for the polar diameter
2. (a) 388 miles
   (b) 1.6% error
3. curvature of the earth
4. Answers will vary.

Height of a Mountainous Island in China

Reproducible 29

ANSWERS

1.
2. $y = 1{,}255$ bu, or 4 li 55 bu (300 bu = 1 li).
   $x = 30{,}750$ bu = 102 li 150 bu.

Similar Triangles in Egypt

Reproducible 30

ANSWERS

Ancient

1. $3\frac{1}{3}$, $3\frac{1}{2}$, $3\frac{3}{8}$, $4\frac{1}{2}$
2. 5.2, 2.6 cubits

Medieval

1. 32.36067978 units

Restoring a Nubian Pyramid

Reproducible 31

ANSWERS

1. 37 ft, 11.28 m
2. $h = 33.8$ ft, 10.3 m
3. 2.25

Mathematics of the Quadrant

Reproducible 32

ANSWERS

2. $AD = 10.9$ cm, $BC = 19.8$ m

Measuring the Earth's Circumference

Eratosthenes was born in Cyrene, a city in the country now called Libya. By that time, Greek mathematics had merged with the ancient mathematics of North Africa and western Asia. Eratosthenes won a high position at the famous university, or museum of Alexandria, and did his best known work in Egypt.

Scientists already knew that the earth was round. As sailboats sailed out to the horizon, people on land lost sight of the bottom of the ship first. The masts were the last part that was visible. Eratosthenes wanted to know how large the earth's circumference was.

Eratosthenes had a brilliant idea. He knew that on June 21 the sun would be directly overhead and cast no shadow at Aswan. At the same moment, the sun would cast shadows in Alexandria, about 600 miles north of Aswan. So at noon on June 21, in the year 230 B.C.E., Eratosthenes measured the height of a pole and the length of its shadow in Alexandria. He found that $\angle 1$ measured about 7.2°. He used the fact that sun's rays are parallel and that alternate interior angles of parallel lines are congruent to show that $\angle 1 \cong \angle 2$. Therefore, the measure of $\angle 2 = 7.2°$, $\frac{1}{50}$ of a circle.

Taking the distance between Alexandria and Aswan as 5000 stades, Eratosthenes found the circumference of the earth from this proportion:

$$\frac{7.2}{360} = \frac{5000}{\text{circumference of Earth}}$$

Eratosthenes found the circumference of the earth to be 250,000 stades. It is believed that he took 1 stade as equal to 300 royal cubits. The royal cubit is 0.525 m long. That gave Eratosthenes a very accurate value for the circumference of the earth.

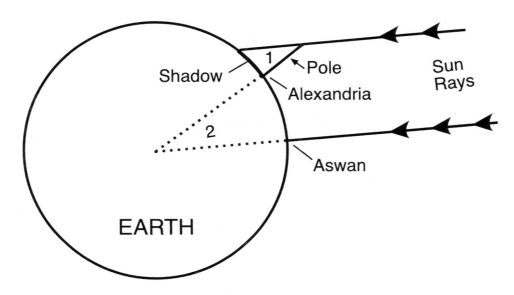

Proportionally, the pole and shadow are much shorter than shown.

(continued)

Geometry Activities from Many Cultures

Measuring the Earth's Circumference *(continued)*

▭ ▭ ▭ ▭ ▭ ▭ ▭ ▭ ▭ ▭ ▭

Questions for Critical Thinking

1. Use Eratosthenes's calculation of 250,000 stades as the diameter of the earth and the conversion factors 1 stade = 300 royal cubits, and 1 royal cubit = 0.525 m, to find:

   (a) The equivalent, in kilometers and in miles, for Eratosthenes's figure for the circumference of the earth.

   (b) The diameter of the earth, according to Eratosthenes.

2. The circumference of the earth measured around the poles is given today as 24,859 miles.
   (a) How big was Eratosthenes's error?

   (b) What was his percent error?

3. Why did the sun cast shadows in Alexandria but not at Aswan on noon of June 21?

4. Why do you think Eratosthenes wanted to measure the earth?

Height of a Mountainous Island in China

An ancient Chinese surveying problem asks for the height and distance from shore of a mountainous sea island. The solution to the problem is given in the *Haidao Suanjing*, translated by Frank Swetz. The idea is to find the height of the mountain without climbing it and the distance to the island without getting wet.

The solution begins "Now for looking at a sea island, erect two poles of the same height." The basic unit of length used here is the Chinese bu, about 1.8 m.

Two vertical poles, each 5 bu high, are placed on the ground 1,000 bu apart, aligned to sight the top of the island. When a surveyor moves back 123 bu from the first pole, the surveyor can sight the island top in line with the pole. To sight the island top in line with the second pole, the surveyor steps back 127 bu behind the second pole. (Ignore the height of the surveyor.)

How high is the top of the mountainous sea island, and how far is it from the first pole? *Method:* Draw a diagram and use proportions derived from similar triangles.

after Needham, 1959

1. On a separate piece of paper, prove that:

   $\triangle BCD \sim \triangle ACE$, and
   $\triangle FGH \sim \triangle AGE$

2. Solve the following proportions.

   Here x = distance of island from the first pole, and y = height of mountain.

$$\frac{y}{x + 123} = \frac{5}{123} \qquad \frac{y}{x + 1,127} = \frac{5}{127}$$

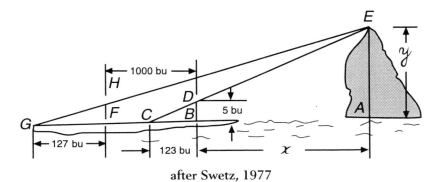

after Swetz, 1977

Geometry Activities from Many Cultures

Similar Triangles in Egypt

ANCIENT EGYPT

Students in ancient Egypt studied geometry to solve practical problems. Geometry provided answers for questions that arose in surveying and in construction of the pyramids and temples. The properties of similar triangles were used by mathematicians, artists, and architects in their daily work.

1. In 1650 B.C.E., the scribe Ah'mose copied a mathematical papyrus that was already 200 years old. He drew the diagram shown here. Given that line segments $\overline{DE} \,||\, \overline{FG} \,||\, \overline{BC}$, lengths of $\overline{DF}$ and $\overline{FB}$ are $3\frac{1}{2}$ cubits, and length of $\overline{DE}$ is $2\frac{1}{4}$ cubits, find the lengths of segments $\overline{EG}$, $\overline{GC}$, $\overline{FG}$, and $\overline{BC}$.

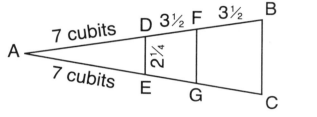

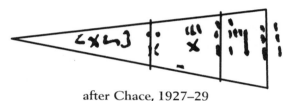

after Chace, 1927–29

Lengths in cubits: EG = _____ GC = _____
                    FG = _____ BC = _____

2. The first Egyptian stone pyramid did not have the true pyramid shape but rose in steps, each step set back from the step below. The steps at King Huni's pyramid at Meydum were filled in, creating a true pyramid shape. To assure smooth sides, each step had to have the same slope. Use your knowledge of similar triangles to fill in the blanks:

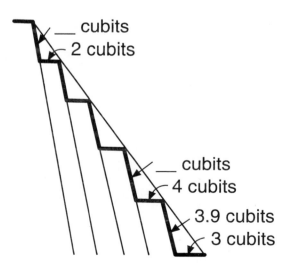

Detail from a cross section of Pyramid at Meydum
(Lengths are approximate.)

(continued)

© 1997 Beatrice Lumpkin
J. Weston Walch, Publisher

Geometry Activities from Many Cultures

Name _____

Date _____

Similar Triangles in Egypt (*continued*)

MEDIEVAL EGYPT

Abu Kamil, born 850 C.E. and known as The Egyptian Calculator, wrote a book called *On the Pentagon and Decagon*. He applied algebra to geometry to solve problems such as:

"A regular decagon is inscribed in a circle. The sides of the decagon measure 10 units. What is the length of the diameter of the circle?"

Abu Kamil's formula gave the diameter as $D = a + a\sqrt{5}$, where a was the length of a side.

1. Use Abu Kamil's formula to solve the example given above.

    D = _____

2. Write an informal proof of Abu Kamil's formula. Refer to this diagram.

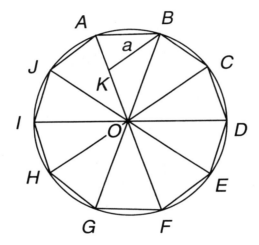

Given regular decagon *ABCDEFGHIJ*, inscribed in a circle with center O and diameter *d*, Prove that $d = a + a\sqrt{5}$.

Hints:

1. Draw $\overline{BK} \cong \overline{AB}$.
2. Find the measures of all of the angles in $\triangle ABK$, $\triangle AOB$ and $\triangle KBO$ to show that all three triangles are isosceles. Also two of the triangles are similar; $\overline{KO} \cong \overline{KB}$.
3. Set up proportions with the corresponding sides.

$$\frac{OB}{BK} = \frac{AB}{AK}$$

   Let $a = AB = BK$, and let $r = OA = OB$. Then $r/a = a/(r - a)$.

4. Use the quadratic formula, just as Abu Kamil did, to find *r*, the radius.

   $r = (^1/_2)(a + a\sqrt{5})$ and $d = 2r = a + a\sqrt{5}$ as required.

Geometry Activities from Many Cultures

Restoring a Nubian Pyramid

Some great monuments left by ancient civilizations have been restored by modern scientists and technicians. Often the reconstruction relies on geometry to get it right. Unfortunately, some of the destruction is recent, the result of greed and ignorance. That has been the sad fate of a number of the fine pyramids of Nubia. The Nubians lived, and still live, in the Sudan and Southern Egypt. They built many pyramids near their ancient capitals of Napata and Meroe (pronounced Mer-o-ay).

In the 1830's, Dr. Joseph Ferlini, a foreign medical officer in the Egyptian army, began to hunt for treasure buried in the Nubian pyramids. Unfortunately, Ferlini's method of treasure hunting was to start at the top of the pyramid and tear it down, stone by stone. That was heavy work. So Ferlini, and his partner Stefani, hired 300 workers whom they heartily feared and distrusted. When an assistant found statues, gold necklaces, and other jewelry, the laborers tried to take it from him. Stefani wanted to pick up the loot and run, but Ferlini wasn't finished.

The next morning, Ferlini returned to the pyramid to continue his wrecking operation. He picked up a few more valuables. With the pyramid wrecked almost to ground level, Ferlini found an underground structure where he thought the real treasure was buried. So he began to dismiss the workers so he could do his looting undisturbed. The workers refused to leave. That night Ferlini's servant told him the workers were planning to kill the partners while they slept. Ferlini and Stefani escaped during the night with their stolen jewelry, leaving piles of rubble that used to be a pyramid.

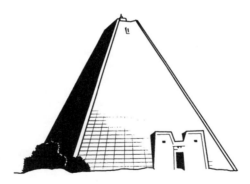

**Queen's Pyramid before it was destroyed by Dr. Ferlini in 1834
after Ahmed Fakhry, 1961**

(continued)

Geometry Activities from Many Cultures

Restoring a Nubian Pyramid *(continued)*

HELP RESTORE A WRECKED PYRAMID

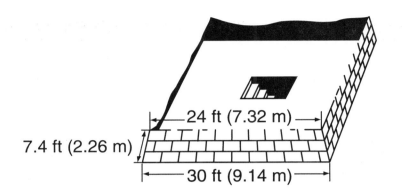

24 ft (7.32 m)

7.4 ft (2.26 m)

30 ft (9.14 m)

Questions for Critical Thinking

The remains of the Nubian queen's pyramid in the above diagram had a base of 30 ft × 30 ft square (9.14 m × 9.14 m). About 7.4 feet (2.26 m), up along the slanting face, the edge of the square cross section was 24 ft (7.32 m). Help the architects restore the pyramid by finding the original dimensions. Use the proportional properties of similar triangles.

1. Find the slant height of the Nubian pyramid.

2. Find the original height of the pyramid.

3. What was the slope of the pyramid?

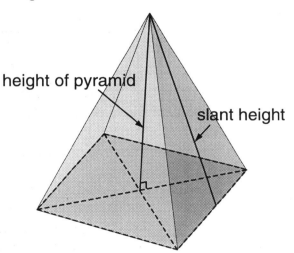

height of pyramid

slant height

Project

Write a short play in which you are with a group of students who plan to spend the winter (summer is too hot) studying the pyramids of Nubia. You go out to visit a queen's pyramid and, to your surprise, the pyramid has been demolished by thieves. What would you think, what would you say, what would you and your classmates do?

Mathematics of the Quadrant

The mathematics of the quadrant was based on the properties of similar triangles. Quadrants were used throughout the Islamic world, from Spain to China. They go back to the astronomer Ptolemy in Egypt about 150, and Hypatia, the great woman mathematician about the year 400 in Egypt. The quadrant was brought to Italy by Leonardo of Pisa and was also used for surveying.

On the following diagram, the dashed line is the line of sight to point B
Quadrant is proportionally smaller than shown.

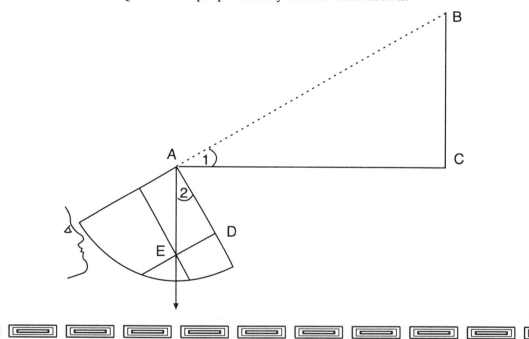

Questions for Critical Thinking

1. Use the properties of angles and similar triangles to write an informal proof that:
   $\angle 1 \cong \angle 2$, $\triangle ABC \sim \triangle AED$, $BC/AC = ED/AD$.

2. If BC is the unknown height of a tall building, the height can be found from the proportion, $BC/AC = ED/AD$. The surveyor can step away from the building, measuring some convenient, known horizontal distance, AC. From scales marked on $\overline{ED}$, and on the plumb line, the lengths ED, and AE, can be read. Then, $AD = \sqrt{AE^2 - ED^2}$.

   What is the height, BC, if $AC = 30$m, $AE = 10.8$ cm, and $ED = 6$ cm? *Hint:* find AD first.

Geometry Activities from Many Cultures

The Right Triangle Theorem

The Babylonian Theorem

Reproducible 33

ANSWERS

1.

a	b	c
120	119	169
3456	3367	4825
4800	4601	6649
1350	1270	1854
0	9	1
72	65	97
360	319	481
2700	2291	3541
960	799	1249
600	481	769
6480	4961	8161
60	45	75
2400	1679	2929
240	161	289
2700	1771	3229
90	56	1106

2. Answers will vary.

Solving Problems in China

Reproducible 36

ANSWERS

1. $12\frac{1}{6}$ chih (435.57 cm)
2. 85.9 cm, or 2 chih 4 tsun
3. 50.5 ft high
4. 8 chih high, 6 chih wide, or 286.4 cm high, 214.8 cm wide
5. Height = 9.6 chih, width = 2.8 chih

Doubling an Area— A Project

Reproducible 38

ANSWERS

1. Yes. Answers will vary.
2. Enlarged square, $(3\sqrt{2})^2 = 18$ cubits^2, is double 9 cubits^2.
3. $1/\sqrt{2}$ or $\sqrt{2}/2$
4. Students will write an informal proof.
5. Answers will vary.
6. (a) 6, 8 cubits
   (b) 12, 16 cubits

Discussion

Babylonian: 1.414213, Indian: 1.414216

Right Triangle Examples from Around the World

Reproducible 39

ANSWERS

1. 164 varas
2. 1 cubit, $\frac{3}{4}$ cubit
3. reed = 13 ft, depth = 12 feet
4. $(z - 144)(z - 25) = 0$ $w = 5, l = 12$
5. Answers will vary.

Examples from Benjamin Banneker

Reproducible 40

ANSWERS

The width of the street is 102.65 ft
1. Radii of a circle are congruent.

2. sss
3. $m\angle B = 60°$, $\overline{OB}$ bisects $\angle B$
4. Altitude bisects base of an isosceles triangle.
5. $\triangle OCB$ is a 30° – 60° – 90° triangle.
6. $\sqrt{c^2 - b^2} = a$
7. $\sqrt{3}\,r$

Explorers of Non-Euclidean Geometry

Reproducible 41

Golden Rectangles: Egyptian

Reproducible 43

ANSWERS

1. 8/5 rectangle is close to the golden ration of 8/4.944

2. Answers will vary. Possible answers: less work to carve narrower widths in the rock. The deeper burial chamber would be darker and more secure.

3. Term   13   21   34   55
   Ratio 1.625 1.615 1.619 1.618
   Term   89   144   233
   Ratio 1.618 1.618 1.618

4. No other pair of reciprocals has this property.

The Babylonian Theorem

Here is a translation of an old Babylonian tablet from about 1900 B.C.E. It looked like an uninteresting list, perhaps sales for the week. Then one day a mathematician looked at the tablet and shouted for joy. The rows list the sides and hypotenuse of right triangles! The Babylonians knew the right triangle theorem 1300 years before Pythagoras was born.

Project

1. Unfortunately, part of the left column had broken off. Find the missing column, a, by using the right triangle formula, $c^2 = a^2 + b^2$.

a	b	c
	119	169
	3367	4825
	4601	6649
	12709	18541
	65	97
	319	481
	2291	3541
	799	1249
	481	769
	4961	8161
	45	75
	1679	2929
	161	289
	1771	3229
	56	106

2. Select any 5 rows and draw a diagram of the triangles you selected. Use graph paper to simplify selection of a convenient scale.

Name _____

Date _____

A Chinese Proof of the Theorem

     Almost 1000 years ago, Bhaskara, the great mathematician from India, produced a proof of the right triangle theorem. The same proof had appeared 1000 years earlier in the *Chiu chang suan shu* (*Nine Chapters on the Mathematical Art*). Perhaps there had been a Chinese–Indian interchange. Or, as the saying goes, "Great minds go in the same direction." This proof still remains one of the best. It is one that you can do with a pair of scissors and a paper card.

Project

Check off each step as you complete it. Work with a partner.

❑   1. Enlarge Diagram 1 on a photocopier and cut it apart. Rearrange parts to prove that $c^2 = a^2 + b^2$.

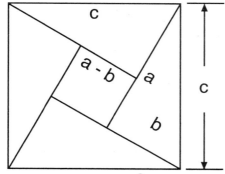

Diagram 1, c^2

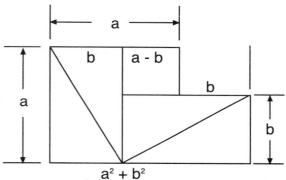

❑   2. Make your own diagram, and do your own construction proof as follows:

    ❑ Fold a card to make four layers.

    ❑ Cut out a right triangle with legs of any ratio, getting four congruent right triangles.

    ❑ Arrange the four triangles to outline a square. Cut out a small square for the center to complete the square of area c^2.

    ❑ Rearrange the square of area c^2 to form square a^2 and square b^2. You have proved that $c^2 = a^2 + b^2$.

❑   3. Repeat the above step 2 but cut out four isosceles right triangles. You will not need to cut out a small square for the center.

Discussion

1. How do you think the Chinese and Indians discovered this proof?

2. What happened to the small center square in step 3?

3. Do you think this proof would work for any right triangle? Why or why not?

Geometry Activities from Many Cultures

Name _____

Date _____

The 3–4–5 Triangle of China

The 3–4–5 triangle was widely used in China. It was a favorite example for teaching problem solving with the right triangle theorem. The following method was credited to Yu the Great, legendary founder of Chinese mathematics and hydraulic engineering. The legend of Yu the Great shows the connection between geometry and Chinese irrigation technology.

Project

MATERIALS

1-cm graph paper, paste, scissors, index cards

Check off each step as you complete it.

☐ 1. Cut a 7 cm × 7 cm square from a sheet of 1-cm graph paper. Paste the square on a piece of card stock to make it easy to handle.

☐ 2. Cut out four 3 cm × 4 cm rectangles. That will leave a 1-cm square. Save all pieces.

☐ 3. Cut each of the 3 cm × 4 cm rectangles on the diagonal. That will make eight right triangles with legs of 3 cm and 4 cm. The length of the diagonal is still not known.

☐ 4. Arrange four of these triangles to outline a 5 cm × 5 cm square. Place the 1-cm square to fill the center.

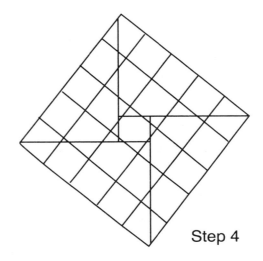

Step 4

☐ 5. Arrange the remaining four triangles around this square to make a 7 cm × 7 cm square. The area of the 7 cm × 7 cm square is ___cm². The area of the four triangles added in this step is _____ cm². Subtract to get the area of the square formed in step 4. You should get 25 cm², proving that the hypotenuse of the 3-4 right triangle is 5.

☐ 6. Remove the outer four triangles added in step 5. Rearrange the remaining four triangles and the 1-cm square for another proof that the hypotenuse of a 3-4 right triangle is 5.

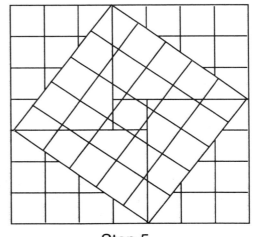

Step 5

Geometry Activities from Many Cultures

Solving Problems in China

For old Chinese measures, 1 tsun = 3.58 cm, about 1.4 in. There are 10 tsun in 1 chih, so 1 chih = 35.8 cm, about 14 in. Use the right triangle theorem to find solutions for these examples.

1. A rope tied to the top of a pole is 3 chih (107.4 cm) longer than the pole. Pulled taut, the end of the rope touches the ground 8 chih (286.4 cm) from the bottom of the pole. Find the length of the pole.

   Hint: Draw a diagram. Then use the right triangle theorem.

2. Boards that are 7 tsun (25 cm) thick are to be cut from a round log of diameter 25 tsun (89.5 cm).What is the widest board that can be cut?

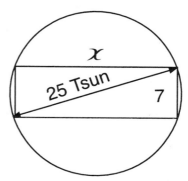

3. A pole leans against a wall that is 10 chih high. The top of the pole touches the top of the wall. If the bottom of the pole is moved 1 chih further from the wall, the pole will fall. How long is the pole?

   Hint: Draw a diagram. Let *x* = the original distance from the bottom of the pole to the wall.

4. A measuring rod of unknown length is used to measure a door. The rod is 4 chih longer than the width of the door, 2 chih longer than the height, and the same length as the diagonal of the door. Find the height and width of the door.

(continued)

Name _____

Date _____

Solving Problems in China *(continued)*

5. The height of a door is 6.8 chih more than the width. The diagonal is 10 chih. Find the height and width using the right triangle theorem and algebra.

Project

A special formula was developed in ancient China to use for examples where the hypotenuse and the difference between the legs are given. The method can be used for any right triangle, although the triangles shown in the following diagram are 3–4–5 triangles.

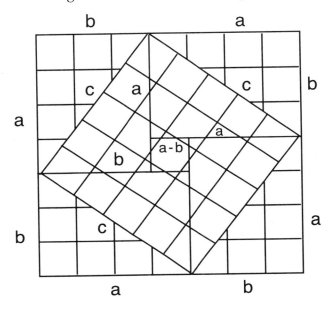

Check off these steps when completed.

- ❑ 1. Make 2 copies of the above diagram.
- ❑ 2. Cut apart the large square. Rearrange the parts to prove:
  $(a + b)^2 = 4ab + (a–b)^2.$
- ❑ 3. Cut apart the medium square. Rearrange the parts to prove:
  $c^2 = 4(\frac{1}{2})ab + (a–b)^2.$
- ❑ 4. Use algebra to transpose, then double both sides to get $4ab = 2(c^2 – (a–b)^2)$:
  Substitute $4ab = 2(c^2 – (a–b)^2)$ for $4ab$ in step 2.
  $(a + b)^2 = 2c^2 – (a–b)^2.$
  $a + b = \sqrt{2c^2 – (a – b)^2}.$
- ❑ 5. Use the formula from step 4 to solve example 5 at top of page.

Geometry Activities from Many Cultures

Right Triangles in Ancient Egypt

The surveyors of ancient Egypt were known as "rope stretchers" because long lengths of ropes were used to measure distances. The ropes were specially made, some with as many as 100 strands to maintain their true length. Knots in the ropes gave the markings in cubits, the Egyptian unit of length.

According to tradition, the knotted ropes could be bent to form a 3–4–5 triangle. Although no written account of this method has survived, many 3–4–5 triangles are part of the design of Egyptian monuments. Mathematicians have also tried to explain how the Egyptians were able to build such marvelously accurate right angles at the corners of some pyramids. For example, the right angles at the base of Khufu's pyramid at Giza have an error of only 1 part in 27,000!

Group Project

Materials: 22 ft. solid, electric wire, 14 – 16 gage, wire cutters, meter stick, masking tape

Check off each step as you complete it.

❏ 1. Mark off 12 cubit lengths on the wire. (The Egyptian royal cubit is about 52.5 cm.) All students working on the project should check to make sure the measurements are correct. Then cut off any excess wire beyond the 12 cubit length.

❏ 2. Tape one end of the wire to the floor. One student should check the end of the wire to make sure it does not move.

❏ 3. Bend the wire at 3 cubits from the end to form a right angle. Then tape the wire to the floor at the 3 cubit mark. One student should watch the wire to make sure it does not move.

❏ 4. Bend the wire at 4 more cubits to form a triangle. One student should hold the wire in position on the floor while the fourth student carries the end of the 12-cubit wire back to the starting point. It should meet exactly to form a 3-4-5 triangle.

❏ 5. Increase the angle between the legs. What happens to your triangle?

❏ 6. Decrease the angle between the legs. What happens to your triangle?

Discussion

1. Must a 3–4–5 triangle be a right triangle? Why or why not?

2. What theorem(s) did you demonstrate in this project?

3. If you had doubled all the sides to 6–8–10 cubits, how would the larger triangle compare to the 3–4–5 triangle.

   (a) Would they be similar?

   (b) Would they be congruent?

   (c) The area of the 6–8–10 triangle would be ___ times larger than the 3–4–5 triangle.

Name _____

Date _____

Doubling an Area

In 800 B.C.E., one of the earliest books in India said: The rope which is stretched across the diagonal of a square produces an area double the size of the original square.

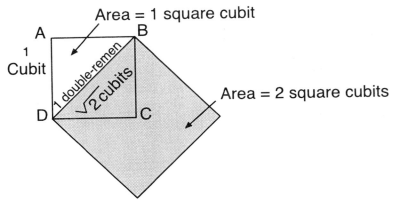

Shaded area is double the area of ABCD

Many hundreds of years earlier, the Egyptians built this idea of doubling areas into their measuring system. They called the side of a unit-square 1-cubit. The diagonal was named "double remen," which is $\sqrt{2}$ cubits long.

Questions for Critical Thinking

1. Is it true that a square whose side is the diagonal of a smaller square is twice the area of the smaller square? Give two examples to support your argument.

2. A square with sides 3 cubits long is enlarged to a square with sides 3 double-remens long. How does the area of the enlarged square compare to the area of the original square?

3. If a square has a diagonal that is 1 cubit long, what is the length of the side of the square?

(continued)

Geometry Activities from Many Cultures

Doubling an Area *(continued)*

Thousands of years ago, in Africa and Asia, people were experimenting with the addition of two squares. In India, brick masons may have discovered the right triangle theorem because brick altars were built to strict mathematical guidelines.

An example from India, from about 700 B.C.E., gives a clever way to add 2 squares. The right triangle theorem is used to design this simple but elegant method.

Method: To add two squares, mark off the side of the smaller on a side of the larger square. Complete the triangle by drawing the hypotenuse. This hypotenuse is the side of the required square.

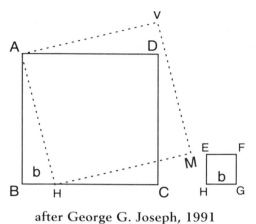

after George G. Joseph, 1991

Questions for Critical Thinking

4. Write an informal proof on a separate page to justify the method of adding two squares. shown in the above diagram.

5. Draw a new diagram in which you modify the diagram on this page so that the two squares that you add are equal in area. Describe your result.

6. Two very old Egyptian problems from the Berlin Papyrus (1800 B.C.E.) also concern a square that is the sum of two squares. You are given the square that is the sum and must find the two smaller squares:

   (a) The sum of two squares is a square of 100 cubits^2. The side of the smaller square is $\frac{3}{4}$ the length of the other small square. What is the length of the sides of the two squares?

   (b) The sum of two squares is a square of 400 cubits^2. The side of the smaller square is $\frac{3}{4}$ the length of the other small square. What is the length of the sides of the two squares?

(continued)

© 1997 Beatrice Lumpkin
J. Weston Walch, Publisher

73

Geometry Activities from Many Cultures

Doubling an Area *(continued)*

To double a square, said the old Indian wise man named Baudahyana, use the diagonal of the square. The diagonal of a 1 *pada* (Indian foot) square is $\sqrt{2}$ *padas* long. To assure accuracy, the ancient Indian builders needed to evaluate $\sqrt{2}$. They found a remarkably good formula. They knew that if they doubled a unit square, the side of the new square would give them the value of $\sqrt{2}$.

Project

MATERIALS

scissors, 2 enlarged copies of a square.

Check off each step as you complete it.

☐ 1. On a separate sheet, make two enlarged copies of square *ABCD*. Label one *ABCD* (side = 1 unit). Label the other square *EFGH*.

☐ 2. Divide *EFGH* into thirds. Divide one of the thirds into thirds again. Divide two of these pieces into fourths, as shown.

☐ 3. Cut *EFGH* apart. Rearrange the parts around *ABCD* as shown. To complete the enlarged square, shade in the corner at *L*.

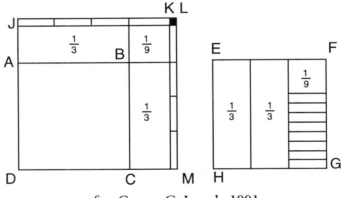

after George G. Joseph, 1991

☐ 4. The enlarged square, minus the small shaded area, is double the area of *ABCD*. The length of the side *JL* is a small amount larger than $\sqrt{2}$. We can approximate $JL \approx \sqrt{2}$ as:

$\sqrt{2} = 1 + 1/3 + 1/(3)(4)$

For greater accuracy, the Indian mathematicians could have sliced a tiny strip off the bottom and side of *DJLM*. This would have given an approximate value of

$\sqrt{2} = 1 + 1/3 + 1/(3)(4) - 1/(3)(4)(34)$.

Discussion

Compare the Indian value for $\sqrt{2}$ with the earlier Babylonian approximation:

$\sqrt{2} = 1 + 24/60 + 51/3600 + 10/216,000$.

Geometry Activities from Many Cultures

Right Triangle Examples from Around the World

1. **Guatemala.** In 1731, Juan Joseph de Padilla wrote a textbook which asked:

   If a plaza is 112 varas wide and 120 varas long, what is the shortest distance between opposite corners of the plaza? (One vara was about 0.838 m.)

2. **Babylonia.** Iraqi archaeologists found a tablet from 1000 B.C.E. at a dig at Tel Dhibayi (Arabic for Mound of the Hyenas). Perhaps 3000 years ago the site was a school because the tablet had the following example.

   Find the length and width of a rectangle, given that the diagonal is $\frac{5}{4}$ cubits and the area is $\frac{3}{4}$ square cubit.

3. **India and China.** In a square pond 10 ft on each side, the top of a reed growing in the center rose 1 ft above the water. The top of the reed was pulled towards shore, just reaching shore. Find the depth of water and the length or the reed.

4. **Egypt.** The Cairo mathematical papyrus asks for the dimensions of a rectangle with area of 60 cubits^2 and a diagonal of 13 cubits. (One cubit was about 0.525 m.)

5. **India.** How can you construct a square that's the difference of two given squares? About 700 B.C.E., the following solution was given in the Indian *Sulbasutras*.

   On the base of the large square *ABCD*, of side a, lay off point *J* so $AJ = b$, the side of the small square *EFGH*. From *J* erect $\overline{JK} \perp \overline{BC}$ and intersecting $\overline{BC}$ at K. With radius $\overline{JK}$ and center at *J*, draw arc *KL* intersecting $\overline{AB}$ at L. Then $AL = e$, the side of the square whose area is the difference between *ABCD* and the smaller square *EFGH*.

   Write an informal proof. *Hint:* Connect $\overline{LJ}$ to form $\triangle AJL$. Show that for $AL = e$, $e^2 = a^2 - b^2$.

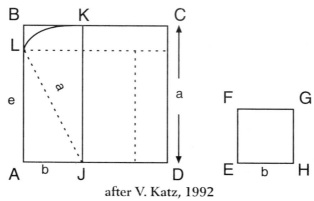

after V. Katz, 1992

Geometry Activities from Many Cultures

Examples from Benjamin Banneker

Benjamin Banneker (1731–1806) is one of the great American heroes of all time. The son and grandson of Africans captured and enslaved, he was fortunate to have been born free. He inherited the family farm, where he worked hard all of his life. As a child he had a few months of schooling. Everything else he had to do on his own. He loved mathematics and science but did not get a chance to learn astronomy until he was in his fifties. Then he performed a near miracle, learning it all in less than a year. In his hand-written journal, he recorded two right triangle examples that interested him. You can solve them here and remember the great man who enjoyed geometry.

On the page in his journal next to the August 1775 astronomy calculations, Banneker wrote, in the style of that time:

Suppose ladder 60 feet long be placed in a Street so as to reach a window on the one Side 37 feet high, and without moving it at bottom, will reach another window on the other side of the Street which is 23 feet high, requiring the breadth of the Street.

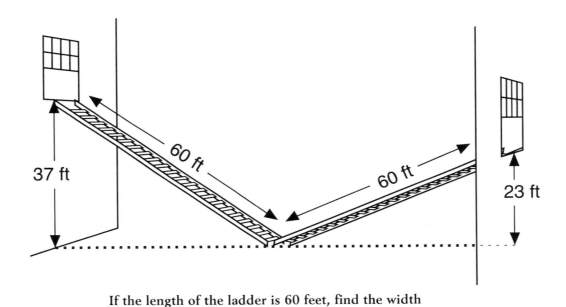

If the length of the ladder is 60 feet, find the width of the street that runs between the buildings.

What is the width of the street? _____

(continued)

Examples from Benjamin Banneker (continued)

The following diagram appears in Banneker's manuscript journal. He wrote:

Required the length of the Sides of an Equilateral Triangle inscribed in a Circle whose Diameter is 200 inches with a general Theorem for all such Questions.

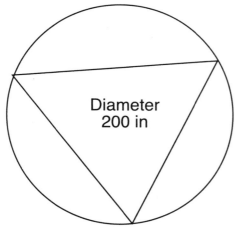

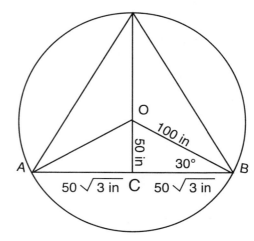

Draw radii to each vertex of the equilateral triangle.

1. The 3 triangles are isosceles because _____

_____

2. The triangles are congruent because _____

_____

3. The m∠OBA = 30° because _____

_____

4. Draw $\overline{OC} \perp \overline{AB}$. AC = CB because _____

_____

5. Since OB = 100 in, half the diameter of 200 in, OC = 50 in because _____

_____

6. $CB = \sqrt{(100 \text{ in})^2 - (50 \text{ in})^2} = 50\sqrt{3}$ in, because _____

   $AB = 2(50\sqrt{3})$ in, or approximately 173.2 in.

7. The general formula for the side of an equilateral triangle inscribed in a circle of radius r, would be _____

Geometry Activities from Many Cultures

Explorers of Non-Euclidean Geometry

Euclid was a mathematician who lived and worked in Alexandria, Egypt, about 300 B.C.E. The right triangle theorem was a basic part of Euclidian geometry, the geometry taught in high schools today. The theorem is based on the parallel postulate, "Only one line, parallel to a given line, can be drawn through a point."

We now know that non-Euclidean spaces are possible. These spaces may have no parallel lines through a point, or they may have many.

Euclidean   **Non-Euclidean**

One parallel line   **No parallel lines**   **Many parallel lines**

One type of non-Euclidean space is based on the surface of a sphere where there are no parallel lines. Here, lines are defined as great circles. For example, look at a world globe. The meridian lines are great circles that are perpendicular to the equator line. But instead of being parallel, the meridians meet at the poles.

Three great Islamic mathematicians of the Middle Ages studied this problem. They were Ibn al-Haytham in Cairo, Egypt (year 1010 C.E.), Umar al-Khayyami in Samarkand, Uzbekistan (1070 C.E.), and Nasir al-Din al-Tusi in Nishapur, Iran (1250 C.E.). Their goal was to prove the right triangle theorem without assuming the parallel postulate. They failed because it could not be done. But their work began the study of non-Euclidean spaces. Al-Din al-Tusi's work was published in Europe and contributed to the mathematics needed for relativity theory.

The Islamic mathematicians studied the following quadrilateral, called the Saccheri quadrilateral. Perhaps it should be called the al-Haytham quadrilateral since Ibn al-Haytham proposed it 400 years before Saccheri was born.

At the endpoints of $\overline{AB}$, erect two congruent perpendiculars, AC and BD. Connect points C and D to complete the quadrilateral. Are angles C and D acute, right, or obtuse angles? These were questions that the mathematicians could not answer without using the same thing they were trying to prove—the parallel postulate.

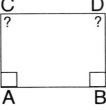

(continued)

Geometry Activities from Many Cultures

Explorers of Non-Euclidean Geometry *(continued)*

INVESTIGATE A GEOMETRY WITH NO PARALLEL LINES

Asian and African explorers of new geometries opened the way for relativity theory and space travel. In 1854, a non-Euclidean geometry, confined to the surface of a sphere, was proposed by Bernhard Riemann. In this geometry, the lines are the great circles of the sphere and points occur in pairs. There are no parallel lines because all great circles intersect. This non-Euclidean geometry by Riemann is different from the spherical geometry of Euclid.

The following experiment can help you decide if the right triangle theorem holds in a geometry based on the surface of a sphere.

Experiment

MATERIALS

1-cm graph paper, world globe or large round ball, masking tape, scissors, straightedge with centimeters, protractor (preferably the flexible type)

Check off each step as you complete it. Work with a partner.

❑ 1. On 1-cm graph paper, draw a 3-4-5 triangle with sides 12 cm, 16 cm, and 20 cm.

❑ 2. Try to tape it onto the globe. If you have a problem, it's the same problem map-makers must overcome in mapping the spherical Earth on flat paper. Remove the triangle.

❑ 3. Cut out the two legs of 12 cm and 16 cm, leaving a thin strip on each side.

❑ 4. Tape your right-angle cutout on a large, round ball. Be careful to preserve the right angle.

❑ 5. With a thin strip of graph paper, measure and record the length needed to complete the right triangle. Tape the strip in place.

❑ 6. With a flexible protractor, measure the three angles of the triangle you just formed. What is their sum?

Discussion

How did your triangle differ from a 3-4-5 triangle?

1. Was the third side of the triangle 20 cm? Does $c^2 = a^2 + b^2$ on the surface of a sphere?

2. Discuss the sum of the three angles of a plane triangle.

   (a) What is the sum of the angles of a triangle in a Euclidean plane? Can a plane triangle have two right angles? Why or why not?

   (b) What was the sum of the angles of the triangle that you formed on the sphere?

   (c) On a globe of the earth, are there any triangles with two right angles? *Hint:* Look at triangles that have bases on the equator and two meridians for sides.

Geometry Activities from Many Cultures

Name _____

Date _____

Golden Rectangles

The golden rectangle has sides in the ratio of 1.618 to 1. It was called "golden" because people found its proportions pleasing. It occurs in nature and appears in the art and architecture of many cultures, including Native American designs.

Golden Rectangles in Shoshone Art

One example comes from the artwork of the Shoshone Native Americans, long admired by many artists. The Shoshone lived in an area that extended from the desert regions of southern California to the mountains of southern Idaho and western Wyoming. No doubt the beauty of their land helped inspire their artwork.

Some students thought that the rectangles used in Shoshone designs had "golden" proportions. So statisticians decided to test this hypothesis by measuring rectangles used in Shoshone beadwork. In a sample of 20 rectangles, the ratio of the shorter to the longer side varied. But most of the values clustered around 1.618, the ratio for golden rectangles. Based on the statistics, the students accepted the hypothesis that the Shoshone used the golden rectangle as their standard of design.

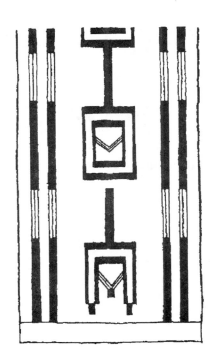

Shoshone pattern

You can explore the geometry of the golden rectangle with the help of the right triangle theorem. You can start by constructing your own golden rectangles.

Class Research Project

Select a cultural item to investigate, such as Dine-Navajo blankets, Senegalese wall hangings, Guatemalan scarves. Measure dimensions of the non-square rectangles and calculate the ratios of the sides. Is the golden rectangle being used in the sample you studied? Is it used sometimes, often, or always?

(continued)

Geometry Activities from Many Cultures

Golden Rectangles *(continued)*

Project

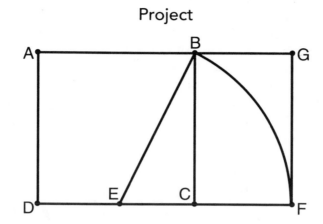

Work with a partner. Check off each step as you complete it.

❏ 1. Draw any square *ABCD* on a piece of graph paper. Find *E*, midpoint of $\overline{DC}$. Draw $\overline{EB}$.

❏ 2. Extend $\overline{DC}$ and extend $\overline{AB}$. Draw an arc with center at *E* and radius *EB* to intersect the extension of $\overline{DC}$ at *F*.

❏ 3. Construct a perpendicular at *F* which intersects the extension of $\overline{AB}$ at *G*.

You now have two golden rectangles, *AGFD*, and *BGFC*.

Discussion and Proof

1. Check your construction by measuring the lengths of the sides. Then calculate the ratios: The sides of a golden rectangle must be in this ratio:

$$\frac{\text{long side}}{\text{short side}} = \frac{\text{short + long sides}}{\text{long side}}$$

2. Use the right triangle theorem and algebra to prove that the rectangles are golden.

   Hints: Let the length of the side of the square equal 1 unit, with $EC = \frac{1}{2}$. Use the right triangle theorem to find length *BE = EF*. Then find the ratios listed above. The ratio is a famous constant, known as φ, the Greek letter phi.

3. Find the reciprocal of the ratio, φ, that you found above. How are φ and its reciprocal related?

Geometry Activities from Many Cultures

Golden Rectangles: Egyptian

Many Egyptian temples were built symmetrically along a long axis. The temple outline was a series of rectangles, decreasing in width until the innermost room was reached. At the end was a deep shaft where the body of the high official was buried.

The rectangle that dominated the design was very close to a golden rectangle. This rectangle circumscribed a special triangle, which some architects called the "Egyptian triangle." The ratio of the height to the base of this triangle was 8 to 5. That gave a ratio of 1.6, very close to the golden-rectangle ratio of 1.618

Alexander Badawy, an Egyptian architect and scholar, found some interesting dimensions in the plans for Egyptian monuments. Starting at the narrow end of the long temples, he found cases where the widths varied in these proportions: 3, 5, 8, 13, 21, 34, 55, 89, . . .

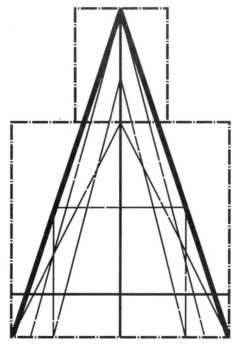

Plan of the sanctuary at Armana, Egypt

Questions for Critical Thinking

1. On graph paper, draw two rectangles. Let the first be exactly 8 × 5 units. Then draw a golden rectangle with long side 8 units and short side 8 × 0.618 units. Compare the two rectangles. Do you notice much difference? How nearly "golden" is an 8 × 5 rectangle?

2. What reasons might the Egyptians have had for building burial temples along a long axis, and narrowing the width as they dug deeper into the rock?

(continued)

Geometry Activities from Many Cultures

Golden Rectangles: Egyptian *(continued)*

3. **An Investigation.** The special sequence of numbers that Badawy found in the dimensions of Egyptian monuments is called the Fibonacci Series in honor of Leonardo of Pisa. In 1220, when Fibonacci returned after years of study in Algeria and Egypt, he brought the advanced mathematics of North Africa to Italy. A riddle he proposed was:

How many pairs of rabbits will there be, if you start with one pair of new born rabbits. These rabbits have the amazing property that when they reach the age of 2 months, they start giving birth to a pair of rabbits every month. The new pair will do the same. From the age of 2 months on, they will also produce a pair of rabbits every month. And so on. That produces a monthly population count of rabbit pairs: 1, 1, 2, 3, 5, 8, . . . , assuming that no rabbits die or quit reproducing. Starting with 3, each term is the sum of the two terms it follows.

Fill out the following table for a Fibonacci sequence. In the second row, give the ratio of the term divided by the preceding term of the series.

Term	1, 1, 2	3	5	8	___	___	___	___	___	___	___
Ratio		1.5	1.66	1.63	___	___	___	___	___	___	___

4. Compare the ratios you found above to the golden ratio, $\phi = 1.618$. Also find $1/\phi$. What special property do these reciprocals have? Find out if any other reciprocals have this property by solving the equation, $1/x = x - 1$.

© 1997 Beatrice Lumpkin
J. Weston Walch, Publisher

Geometry Activities from Many Cultures

Mapmaking

Teacher
Guide
Page

Benjamin Banneker: District of Columbia Surveyor

Reproducible 46

ANSWERS

1. (a) Dark
   (b) Dark
   (c) Light
2. 3 hours later [(121.5–76.6)/360]×24=3
3. 15°

Latitude and Longitude Measure

Reproducible 47

ANSWERS

1. Meridians are not parallel because they all pass through the North and South Poles.
2. Meridians are all the same length, lines of latitude are not.
3. Equator = 0 degrees latitude. North Pole 90°N, South Pole 90°S latitude.

Some Native American Maps

Long before Columbus, many of the Indian nations of the Americas had developed skills as mapmakers. When Columbus was lost off the coast of Central America, a lone Maya fisherman made a map of the region for the Spaniards. The first English settlers in North America also made use of Native American maps.

Lamhatty's map is a famous example of these mapmaking skills. In 1707, a young Native American named Lamhatty was captured near the Florida Gulf Coast. His captors marched him north through territory unknown to him. They were on their way to sell Lamhatty in the English slave markets. The young man escaped and walked for nine more days. Then he surrendered to the English in Virginia, who enslaved him again. When a British officer asked Lamhatty about his 600-mile forced march, he described his journey and drew a very good map.

The story had a happy ending, because when summer came Lamhatty escaped again and remained free.

Group Project

Reconstruct Lamhatty's map from the following description that he gave of his journey. Refer to an atlas to find the rivers and towns he passed on his travels.

1. Lamhatty was captured in his hometown near the Florida Gulf (probably between Pensacola and Panama City). He described it as "the waves tumble and roar like a sea."

2. He was taken north to Abekas on the Coosa River, in what is now Alabama.

3. Next stop was Tallapoosa, Alabama, where he was forced to work in the fields all summer.

4. He traveled east to Oconee on the Oconee River, in what is now Georgia.

5. Then he crossed the Oconee River and walked through southern Appalachia to the headwaters of the Savannah River, in Northeastern Georgia.

6. Lamhatty was then taken north "along the ledge" of the Blue Ridge mountains, probably north through North Carolina, into Virginia.

7. Lamhatty escaped on a branch of the Rappahannock River, probably the Rapidan, "as the river flows out of the mountains." It was north of present-day Charlottesville.

8. He walked east and surrendered to the English in northern Virginia, not far from the present-day District of Columbia.

Geometry Activities from Many Cultures

Navigators of the Pacific

Long before Columbus, the Marshall Islanders learned to navigate hundreds of miles of open sea between Pacific Ocean islands. Their science of navigation required knowledge of star altitudes for different locations, and the effect of wind and wave patterns. For example, an island over the horizon can be detected because waves striking the island are reflected. The reflected wave alters ocean swell patterns up to 80 kilometers out at sea. Birds can also serve as guides. When navigators see birds at sea, they know they are close to an island. If the birds are of a species that returns to land at night, the sailors wait until late afternoon to follow the birds to port.

Some of the small coral islands lie low in the water and are not visible from a distance. Often a cloud mass gathers over these small islands. When navigators spot a cloud, they know it may signal land. Sometimes the reflection of the island is visible on the underside of a cloud. The navigators' knowledge is highly valued. Students who attend schools for future navigators are carefully selected. Maps such as the following are used to teach patterns of the ocean swells—those coming in to the island and those reflected from the island. These maps made of sticks are called Meddo charts. The following example, on display at Chicago's Field Museum, shows the waters between Majuro and Jaliut Atolls in the Republic of Marshall Islands.

STAR MAPS OF PACIFIC ISLANDERS

Long before the Europeans came to their islands, Pacific Islanders had developed their own advanced technology and science. The islanders created special maps to teach wind and wave forms. Since the lives of the crew depended on the navigator's knowledge, young navigators were very good students They learned to steer by the stars, following a star compass which they had memorized. Pacific Islanders found their way across open ocean to islands 700 km away without the aid of a magnetic compass or radio.

(continued)

Geometry Activities from Many Cultures

Navigators of the Pacific *(continued)*

Island astronomers remembered which stars rose on the horizon in the direction of islands they wanted to visit. For each island destination, the Pacific Island navigators followed a whole series of stars, since star positions change as the earth turns. In the Caroline Islands, the star compass, or map, showed the horizon as a big circle. Naturally, their own island was at the center. The circle was divided by radii that point to the rise and set positions of 16 bright stars. These star positions were used to locate lands they often visited.

Gilbert Island students also used a study guide made in the form of stone slabs. The islanders called them the Stones for Voyaging, or Stone Canoes. Each pair of stones also lined up with the rising and setting points of some of their guide stars. For example, at sunset in August, the star Regulus rose and lined up with the stone pointing to Tamana, 80 km away. By midnight, Regulus was in a different position and the star Arcturus lined up with the Tamana stone.

To give more exact positions for star locations, Gilbert Islanders created their own coordinate system for the heavens. They mentally sliced the sphere of the skies with four east–west planes. Then they sliced the sphere parallel to the equator and assigned names to each sector. In all, Pacific Island navigation was an intellectual achievement of the highest order.

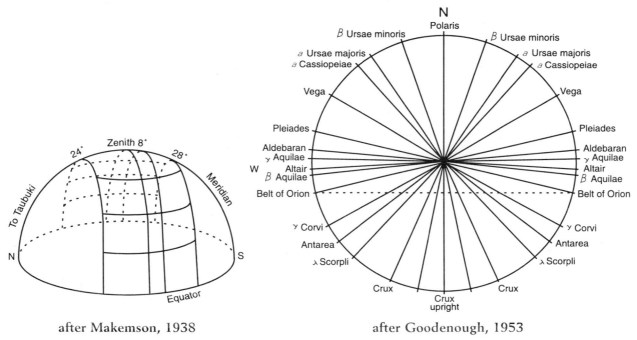

after Makemson, 1938   after Goodenough, 1953

(continued)

Name _____

Date _____

Navigators of the Pacific *(continued)*

Questions for Critical Thinking

1. In what ways was Pacific Island navigation scientific?

2. The skill of the island navigators depended, in part, on the navigator's excellent memory. How important is a good memory in your schoolwork? Do you think it was easy or hard for the islanders to memorize their lessons? Explain.

3. Which of the stars in the Caroline Island map can be seen in your location? *Hint:* "Stars Visible at Dusk" are often listed on the weather page of daily newspapers.

4. Using words only—no numbers—write a description that locates a given object in the classroom. The path to the object can start from the front door of the classroom.

Group Project

Visit a lake, river, or ocean shoreline. Discuss the best way to make a map of several miles of the shoreline. Divide up the sectors to be mapped among group members. Put the map together and submit it to your class for discussion.

Geometry Activities from Many Cultures

Benjamin Banneker: District of Columbia Surveyor

Benjamin Banneker was one of the earliest, practicing mathematicians in the United States. As a child in the 1730's, he attended a country school in Maryland. Everything else, algebra, trigonometry, and astronomy, he had to learn on his own. Banneker's genius led to his appointment as astronomer for the survey team to plan the city of Washington, D.C. He is also famous for his almanacs. Local almanacs gave the time of sunrise and sunset, moonrise and moonset, planetary positions, times of eclipses, tides, and so on. The time for these events depended on the city's latitude and longitude.

LONGITUDE AND LATITUDE

The longitude and latitude of Baltimore entered all of Banneker's calculations for his almanac. Longitude and latitude are the coordinates used to locate a point on the surface of the Earth's globe. The axes on the globe are the equator and the Greenwich prime meridian. Latitude is measured north or south from the equator. Longitude is measured east or west from the Greenwich meridian, which goes through London. Meridians appear like vertical lines on the globe but are actually great circles connecting the North and South Poles.

The longitude of Baltimore is 76.6° West. When it is sunrise in London, it is still night in Baltimore. How much later will the sun rise in Baltimore? That depends on how long it takes the Earth to turn 76.6°. Since the Earth turns 360° in 24 hours, it will take (76.6/360)24 hours = 5.1 hours. An adjustment is also needed for latitude because Baltimore is 39.3° north of the equator, while London is 51.3° north of the equator. Banneker completed thousands of calculations, like these, for each almanac.

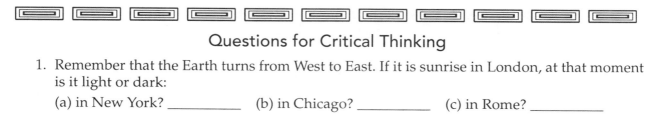

Questions for Critical Thinking

1. Remember that the Earth turns from West to East. If it is sunrise in London, at that moment is it light or dark:

   (a) in New York? _____ (b) in Chicago? _____ (c) in Rome? _____

2. Sacramento, California is about the same latitude north of the Equator as Baltimore. But Baltimore is at longitude 76.6° West and Sacramento is a longitude 121.5° West. When the sun has just begun to rise in Baltimore, it is still night in Sacramento. How much later will the sun rise in Sacramento?

3. The Earth's globe is divided into 24 equal time zones. How many degrees of longitude are there to each time zone?

Latitude and Longitude Measure

Project

MATERIALS

meterstick, white or light-colored sphere with smooth surface (could be plastic sphere, snowball Christmas tree ornament), world globe for reference, string, lettering line-tape or pen and pencil

Check off each step as you complete it.

❏ 1. Study the globe of the earth to observe the longitude and latitude circles. These are imaginary circles people use to locate points on the surface of the earth.

❏ 2. With line-tape or a pen, mark a great circle on a blank globe or sphere to represent the equator. Great circles are the largest circles that go around the globe. Their center is the center of the earth. Mark points not on the equator as north or south of the equator.

❏ 3. At any point on the equator, draw a second great circle perpendicular to the equator. This represents the zero meridian that goes through Greenwich and both poles of the globe. Points not on this meridian will be marked as east or west of Greenwich.

❏ 4. With a flexible tape or string, measure the length of the equator. If you are using a string, use a meterstick to find the length of the string.

❏ 5. Divide the length of the equator into 24 equal parts. Starting with the zero meridian, lightly mark the division points on the equator.

❏ 6. Draw great circles at each of the points marked on the equator, perpendicular to the equator. These circles must pass through both the North and the South Poles. The circles you have just drawn represent the meridians.

❏ 7. On a meridian, mark a point about 23.5° north of the equator, which is about $\frac{1}{4}$ of the distance from the equator to the North Pole. Through this point, draw a circle parallel to the equator. This is not a great circle. This line represents the tropic of Capricorn, the most northerly latitude in which the sun is directly overhead at noon on June 21.

❏ 8. Repeat step 7 but mark a point about 23.5° south of the equator, about $\frac{1}{4}$ of the distance from the equator to the South Pole. Through this point, draw a circle parallel to the equator. This line represents the tropic of Cancer, the most southerly latitude in which the sun is directly overhead at noon on December 21.

Class Discussion

1. Are the meridians parallel? Why or why not?

2. Are all the meridians the same length? Are all of the circles of latitude the same length?

3. What are the latitudes of the equator, the North Pole, and the South Pole?

Geometry Activities from Many Cultures

Geometry in Architecture

African Influences on American Architecture:

Reproducible 50

ANSWERS

1. .67
2. (a) 7.4 ft
   (b) 56%

Lessons from the Pueblo Indians

Reproducible 51

ANSWERS

1. $(3 \times 3 \times 4) + (3 \times 8 \times 6) + (3 \times 3 \times 6) + (2 \times 2.5 \times 4) + (4.3 \times 3 \times 8) + (6 \times 4.3 \times 2.5) + (4 \times 4.3 \times 2.5) + (8 \times 6 \times 4.3) = 671.1m^3$
2. $(8 \times 14.6) + (4 \times 3) = 112.8m^2$

Circles in Architecture

Reproducible 54

ANSWERS

2. Answers will vary. Ideal values in unit squares are:
   (a) 197   (e) 309
   (b) 256   (f) 315
   (c) varies   (g) 326
   (d) 296

Name _____

Date _____

Geometry in Architecture

Modern housing has many advantages: central heating and air conditioning and modern appliances. But it is expensive and may not be suited to local conditions. Architects are now studying traditional housing of the original peoples of Africa, Asia, the Pacific Islands, and the Americas. The older building designs met these goals:

1. Protection from extremes of climate—heat, cold, wind, rain, and snow
2. Use of renewable materials, available locally
3. Beauty and service

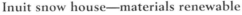

Inuit snow house—materials renewable

Decorated Mangbettu house—sheds heavy rains

CARPENTERS' TOOLS FROM EGYPT

The geometry of the ancient builders began with their tools. The basics of a modern carpenter's tool kit were already in use 5000 years ago in Egypt. These tools included plumb lines, carpenters' levels, squares, measures of length, hammers, chisels, planing devices, and saws.

The plumb line is based on properties of perpendicular lines. It provided a true vertical line to keep brick walls straight. Ancient Egyptians used the plumb line to invent a carpenter's level. They knew that a plumb line is perpendicular to a true horizontal line.

PLUMB LINE PROJECT

MATERIALS: string, small weight

Check off each step as you complete it.

❑ 1. Attach a weight to a string to make a plumb line.
❑ 2. Let the plumb line hang freely alongside a vertical wall, while two other students check whether the plumb line hangs parallel to the wall.
❑ 3. Suspend the plumb line just above a horizontal surface (floor or desk). Two other students observe the angle that the plumb line would make with the surface if it were actually touching.

Discussion

How can you tell if the wall is straight? Was the surface truly horizontal?

Geometry Activities from Many Cultures

Finding True North

Traditional buildings were often designed to face a particular direction. The Gros Ventres of Montana face the doors of their tepees to the east, to greet the rising sun. The Chinese build their houses facing south, to protect from the north wind and to get as much sunshine as possible in the winter. Temples and pyramids of Central America and Africa lined up with the cardinal directions, north, east, south, and west.

Geometry and astronomy worked hand in hand to find these directions. Once people found true north, the other directions could then be found with the aid of geometry. In Egypt, Papua, and many other lands, people found north by using a shadow compass and some geometry. You can easily model this method.

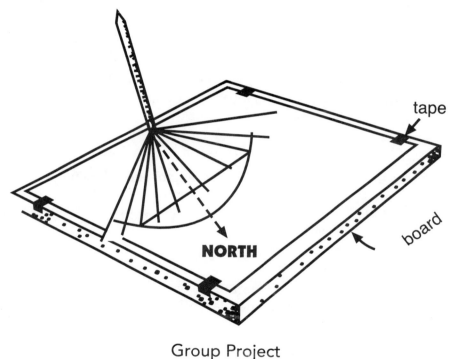

Group Project

Take the following steps to make a shadow compass. Group members should alternate as time-keepers and recorders. Check off each step as you complete it.

MATERIALS

polystyrene board, chopstick, watch, tape, felt-tipped pen, paper, compass, chalk, plumb line

❑ 1. With the small end of a chopstick, poke a hole in a board near the center of one edge. Make a corresponding hole in a piece of paper.

(continued)

Geometry Activities from Many Cultures

Finding True North *(continued)*

❑ 2. Push the large end of the chopstick into the hole and glue, if necessary to keep firmly erect. The line of the stick should make a right angle with the board. Poke a hole in the paper and push it down the stick and onto the board. Then tape or tack the paper to the board. Outline the paper on the board.

❑ 3. On a sunny day, place the board outdoors in a level, sunlit area where it will not be disturbed. Outline the board position with chalk. Use the plumb line to check that the chopstick is truly vertical.

❑ 4. At 10-minute intervals, about 11 am to 1 pm (or 12–2 pm daylight savings time) mark the end point of the shadow of the stick on the paper. Do not move the paper or the board until this step is complete.

❑ 5. Select two shadows that appear to be the same length, one before noon and one after noon. Confirm your choice by making an arc with a compass centered at the stick hole, and with radius equal to the shadows you selected. Connect the endpoints of these two equal-length shadows.

❑ 6. Find the midpoint of the segment connecting the endpoints. The line from this midpoint to the stick hole is the true north–south line, also called the meridian. A line perpendicular to this line gives the east–west direction. *Note:* If you removed the paper to do steps 5 and 6, be sure to replace it on the board in the exact same position.

African Influences on American Architecture

New Orleans is proud of its historic "shotgun" houses. This style was practical in warm climates. One room opened into the next along a straight axis. Breezes could sweep right through and windows offered cross ventilation. The original design of the shotgun house came from Angola, Africa. The design was brought to New Orleans and other southern cities by free Haitians. In Haiti, many shotgun houses had been built after the Angolan style by families who had come to Haiti from the southwest coast of Africa.

Another African contribution to architecture is now considered "as American as apple pie." Many Americans, at one time or another, have lived in a house with a porch. Who brought the porch to North America? It was not the Europeans. Neither the British Isles, France, nor Spain built homes with porches. Few realize that when Africans were first brought to places like the Carolinas, there was no housing for them and no large-scale agriculture. The captive Africans had no choice but to build housing. They built West African style housing, housing which included porches. They also taught the British how to grow rice, a staple crop in West Africa.

1. Find the slope of the roof. A shotgun house has a roof which forms an isosceles triangle above the front wall. The front wall is a square, 15 ft × 15 ft, and the height of the peak of the roof is 20 ft. What is the slope of the roof over the side walls?

2. Add a porch to a golden-rect-angular house. A family lives in a 30 ft wide by 48.5 ft house. These dimensions are close to a golden rectangle. The family wants to add a front and side "wrap-around" porch without changing the proportions of the house.

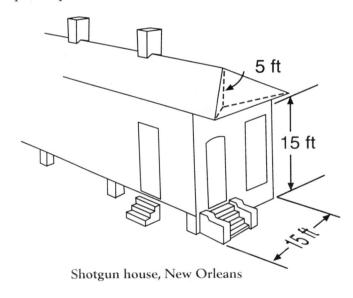

Shotgun house, New Orleans

5 ft

15 ft

15 ft

(a) If the front porch is to be 12 ft deep, how wide should the side porch be? *Hint:* Draw a diagram, then set up a proportion.

(b) By what percent is the area of the house increased by adding the porch area to the house area?

Geometry Activities from Many Cultures

Lessons from the Pueblo Indians

Modern architects are learning lessons from the housing designs of the people called "pueblo" by Spaniards, who conquered them after very fierce fighting. Pueblo means village, people, or nation in Spanish. It was the village-type of multifamily housing that prompted the Spaniards to call the Zuni, Hopi, Acomas, and related peoples "pueblo." Many features of pueblo housing are still of interest and have inspired new types of modern apartment buildings. These new ideas in housing are important because the human race is running out of space, and land that is arable (suitable for agriculture).

The Pueblo architects overcame a number of problems. The first problem was heat regulation. The thick adobe bricks absorb sun during the hot days, and reradiate heat into the house during the cold nights. Land was conserved by building up instead of out and leaving no space between housing units. By concentrating the housing on a minimum land area, resources were centralized and shared. These resources included water, defense, culture, and education. Privacy was preserved by giving each family a private entrance and an unobstructed view.

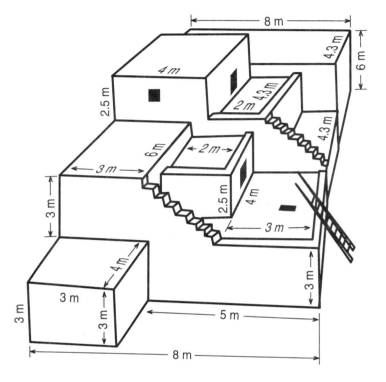

Questions for Critical Thinking

1. In the above illustration, what is the total volume of the part of the pueblo shown?

2. The roofs of the one-story units provided extra space for work or social purposes. What was the total area provided by the flat roofs?

    Hint: Look at the top view.

Geometry Activities from Many Cultures

Geometry in Mozambique

Professor Gerdes was teaching college students in the southeast African country of Mozambique. He was explaining the geometry used in weaving baskets. A student objected:

"People who have not gone to school don't know any mathematics."

Dr. Gerdes challenged the student. "What shape are the houses in your village?"

"We build rectangular-shaped houses in my village," the student replied.

"And how do they start the construction?" the professor continued.

"That's easy. They take two equal-length ropes, tied together at their centers. Then they nail two ends in the ground for the corners of one side wall. Two people pull the other ends of the ropes tight to mark the other two corners."

"Isn't that geometry?" the professor demanded.

Questions for Critical Thinking

1. Prove that the professor was right, that the Mozambican method outlined a true rectangle.

   For the following diagram, prove that ABCD is a rectangle, given that AC = BD, AE = EC = BE = ED.

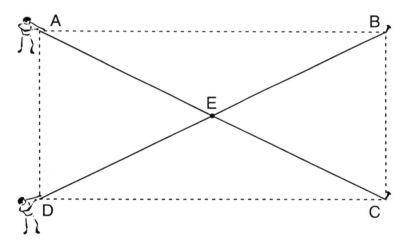

2. Another student in that class gave an alternative method used in his village. Take four poles that are the same lengths as the desired lengths for the walls of the house, and arrange them in what you think is a rectangle. Measure the diagonals. If they are not equal, reposition the poles until the diagonals are equal. Then you will outline a rectangle.

   (a) Prove that ABCD is a rectangle, given that AC = BD, AB = CD, and BC = AD.

   (b) Draw an example to show a case where AC = BD, and AB = CD but the quadrilateral, ABCD, is not a rectangle. *Hint:* Make a toothpick model.

Geometry Activities from Many Cultures

Name _____

Date _____

Circles in Architecture

The circle has long been a basic concept of traditional builders in Africa and North America. For many Native American nations, the circle symbolizes the place of emergence of the human race. Many people admire the beauty of the circle as the symbol of perfection.

The circular shape has many practical advantages. In some parts of Africa, the main building materials are reeds, saplings, and clay. A round shape is easy to form with these flexible materials. On the plains of North America, the round shape of the tepee was easy to roll up when the seasons changed and it was time to move. Another benefit of the round shape was superior wind resistance.

Some claim that circular shapes are also space saving. You will compare polygons and circles of equal length to find the shape that provides the greatest floor space.

Group Project

MATERIALS: Calculator, graph paper, string, masking tape

Divide parts of this investigation among members of your group. Then discuss the findings to reach a group conclusion. Check off each step as you complete it.

❏ 1. For each member of the group, cut a length of string equal to the length of 256 units of your graph paper.

❏ 2. With the string as the given perimeter, form the following figures on your graph paper. Calculate the area of the figures using the appropriate formulas. Make up a table to record the areas in terms of unit squares of your graph paper.

Area

(a) Triangles — three different shapes including an equilateral triangle _____

(b) Rectangles — five different shapes including a square.   _____

(c) Trapezoids (two different shapes.)   _____

(d) Regular hexagon   _____

(e) Regular octagon   _____

(f) Regular decagon   _____

(g) Circle   _____

Discussion

For shapes (a) to (f), which shape has the largest area? Which has the smallest area? Do you notice a trend as the number of sides is increased?

Geometry Activities from Many Cultures

Exploration of an Ellipse

This is a true tale from the crypt. Pharaoh Rameses VI enjoyed only a short rule before he passed from this life. Fortunately his tomb was ready, because work on the tomb started soon after he took office around the year 1130 B.C.E. In the plans for the vault over the crypt, a remarkable full-scale drawing was made on the leveled and whitewashed rock surface. The drawing is the top of a perfect ellipse, still visible on the rock. It showed a cross section of the three-dimensional vault. All the stonecutters had to do to cut an elliptical roof for the crypt was to take the measurements from the drawing.

You can construct a model of this ellipse.

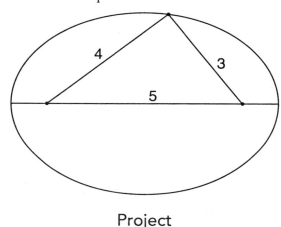

Project

MATERIALS: 10" (25.4 cm) heavy string, graph paper, pencil, tape

Work with a partner. Check off each step as you complete it.

❑   1. Pencil in a horizontal axis, 7 large graph units long, near the center of your paper.

❑   2. Mark a point 1 large unit from each end of the axis. Poke a small hole through the points you just marked. The points should be 5" apart and are the foci of the ellipse.

❑   3. Push an end of the cord through each hole you made. Tape the cord in place on the back of the paper, allowing exactly 7" of the cord to be free between the two holes.

❑   4. Place the point of your pencil inside the cord to pull the cord taut against the paper. While one partner holds the paper in place, the other partner swings the pencil around the page to draw an ellipse. Do not allow the cord to slacken.

❑   5. Change places with your partner, and repeat the above steps.

(continued)

Name _____

Date _____

Exploration of an Ellipse (continued)

1. On the ellipse you constructed, there are four points where the string forms a 3-4-5 triangle with the axis. One point is shown. On the following diagram, mark three more points on the ellipse where the string forms a 3–4–5 triangle with the axis.

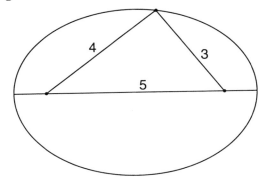

2. The tomb of Rameses VI was dug out of solid rock. Given the width of the burial room, would the elliptical-shaped vault require more or less excavation of stone than a circular vault of the same diameter? Explain, using a diagram.

3. The ellipse is the set of points such that the sum of distances from two fixed points (foci) is equal to a constant. The fixed length of the string in your construction equaled the sum of distances from the foci. You can explore the ellipse by varying the distance between the foci, and varying the length of the string. Construct ellipses using:

Length of string	Distance between foci
7 units	4 units
7 units	6 units
6 units	5 units
10 units	5 units

What changes did you observe as the distance between the foci changed?

What changes did you observe as the length of string changed?

4. If you stand on one focus point of a room with an elliptical ceiling, and a friend stands at the other focus point, your whisper will be heard by your friend. But people elsewhere in the room will not hear you. Why do you think this happens?

Geometry Activities from Many Cultures

Igloo Dome and Andes Bridge

What do the dome of a snow igloo and a hanging bridge in the Andes Mountains have in common? Both make use of the special properties of a curve we call a catenary from the Roman name for a freely hanging chain. It is the most flexible shape, best able to withstand strong Polar winds when inverted for the roof of an igloo. In the hanging position of an Inca rope bridge over a deep canyon, it supports the weight of people and animals. Many modern bridges are also built in the shape of a catenary for strength.

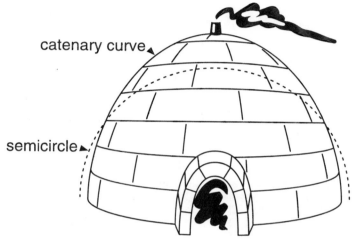

catenary curve

semicircle

Cooperative Project

Take the following steps to draw a catenary curve. Check off each step as you complete it.

❑   1.   Tape a piece of paper to the wall. Tape the ends of a chain to a ruler.

❑   2.   Hold up the ruler in a horizontal position, and let the chain hang freely. Then shine a lamp or flashlight behind the chain to form a shadow of the chain on the paper.

❑   3.   Trace the shadow on the paper with a thin felt-tipped marker or crayon. It will be a catenary curve.

❑   4.   Prove that this curve is not circular.

Hint: Construct the perpendicular bisectors of any two chords connecting two points of the catenary. In a circle, the perpendicular bisector of a chord passes through the center of the circle. Is your curve a circle?

Geometry Activities from Many Cultures

Trigonometry

Trigonometry of African Pyramids

Reproducible 56

ANSWERS

1. (a) 54° 31'
   (b) 43° 20'
2. 132.3 m
3. 105 m (49 m + 56 m)
4. (a) .785
   (b) 51.9°
5. Answers will vary.
6. 32.2 ft

The Measure of Mexico's Pyramid

Reproducible 57

ANSWERS

30; tan 15° = y/x and tan 11.4° = $y/(x + 37)$, x measured to center of pyramid

Trigonometry in Babylonia

Reproducible 58

ANSWERS

a	b	c	c/b	$\sec^{-1}$ c/b, degrees
120	119	169	1.4202	45.21
3456	3367	4825	1.4330	45.75
4800	4601	6649	1.4451	46.21
13500	12709	18541	1.4588	46.73
72	65	97	1.4923	47.93
360	319	481	1.5078	48.46
2700	2291	3541	1.5456	49.68
960	799	1249	1.5632	50.23
600	481	769	1.5987	51.28
6480	4961	8161	1.6450	52.56
60	45	75	1.6667	53.13
2400	1679	2929	1.7446	55.03
240	161	289	1.7950	56.14
2700	1771	3229	1.8232	56.73
90	56	106	1.8929	58.11

Discussion

This appears to be a table of sec values for 45.2° to 58.1°, in steps of approximately 0.5°.

Indian and Islamic Trigonometry

Reproducible 59

Circumference of the Earth

Reproducible 60

ANSWER TO DISCUSSION

The measure of the height of the mountain or the measure of the dip angle might have been sources of error.

The Law of Sines Proved

Reproducible 61

ANSWERS

1. (a) and (b) Answers will vary.
2. Answers will vary.
3. Answers will vary. Calculus was used long before it was placed on a logical scientific foundation.
4. To find parts of a triangle if you know two sides and an angle opposite one of the sides, or two angles and a side.
5. (a) $360° \times \dfrac{56°}{\text{mile}}$ = 20,160 miles
   (b) Al-Biruni's estimate was about 24,900 − 20,160 = 4,740 miles short. The theory was correct, but the small dip angle could not be measured accurately in those times.
6. 20.9m, 14.6m

Banneker and the Law of Sines

Reproducible 63

ANSWERS

15 ft, 30 ft, for either method

Critical Thinking

1. Answers will vary.
2. The accuracy of a construction is limited by the accuracy of measurement tools.
3. Answers will vary.
4. The length of each side is 173.2 in.
5. The general formula is $2\sqrt{3}r$, r the length of the radius.

Trigonometry and Nursing— The Story of Florence Nightingale

Reproducible 64

ANSWERS

| | Rectangular Coordinates Time elapsed, weeks Mortality Rate, %* | |
Week	x	y
Oct. Week 1	1	140
Oct. Week 4	4	103
Nov. Week 4	8	128
Dec. Week 3	11	203
Jan. Week 1	14	216
Jan. Week 2	15	305
Feb. Week 1	18	415
Mar. Week 1	22	215
Apr. Week 1	27	123
Apr. Week 2	28	81
May Week 2	32	53
Jun. Week 2	36	47
Jun. Week 4	38	40

Trigonometry of African Pyramids

Trigonometry began with the pyramids. The first African pyramid was built in large steps, like setting one box on top of another. Each layer was set back from the one under it, for stability and to create a pleasing effect. We call the setback the *run*, and the height of the step, the *rise*. Imhotep, the legendary architect of the first pyramid, selected the ratio of run to rise carefully. Egyptians called this ratio *seked*. It is the inverse of our slope, or *tangent*. Once the size of the base was planned, the seked would determine the pyramid height.

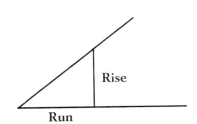

Step pyramid

Soon after Imhotep's success, pyramids were built with smooth sides. The architects had to make sure that all four sides leaned in at the same angle so they would meet on top at a point. They did this by keeping the seked ratio constant. Each pyramid face rose at the same angle, keeping the sides smooth. The seked they selected was about $1\frac{1}{2}$ cubits run to 2 cubits rise. Most of these massive pyramids are still standing, 4600 years later.

An unusual pyramid is the pyramid at Dahshur, known as the Bent Pyramid. It started out as an ordinary pyramid. The square base was 188.6 m per side, and the seked was 0.713. Then something happened. Perhaps the builders found that the rise was too steep, or they had to finish the pyramid in a hurry. The fact is that at a height of 49 m, the seked was suddenly changed to 1.06. That's why it is called the Bent Pyramid.

Bent pyramid

Questions for Critical Thinking

1. **(a)** What was the original angle of inclination of the Bent Pyramid if the original seked, or run/rise ratio, was 0.713?

   (b) What was the new angle of inclination when the seked changed to 1.06?

(continued)

Geometry Activities from Many Cultures

Trigonometry of African Pyramids *(continued)*

2. How tall would the pyramid have been if the run/rise ratio had remained 0.713?

   _____

3. How tall was the Bent Pyramid when it was finished?

   _____

4. The Great Pyramid of Pharaoh Khufu was originally about 481.4 ft, or 146.7 m high. Each side of the square base was about 756 ft, or 230.4m.

   (a) What was its seked?

   _____

   (b) What was the angle of inclination of the sides of the pyramid?

   _____

5. Compare the seked of the Great Pyramid with the seked ratios of the Bent Pyramid. Do you think the builders of the Great Pyramid learned a lesson from the Bent Pyramid? Why or why not?

   _____

   _____

   _____

6. The Nubian and Egyptian civilizations were related, but still distinct cultures. Nubian pyramids also followed a different tradition. The Nubian king Piankhi (now thought to be Piy) ruled both Egypt and Nubia. His pyramid had a base of 26 × 26 ft. The faces of the pyramid rose at an angle of 68°. Calculate the height of his pyramid.

Geometry Activities from Many Cultures

The Measure of Mexico's Pyramids

Kukulkán's pyramid

A high school Spanish class visited the Chichén Itzá pyramid complex in Yucatán, Mexico. The main pyramid rises steeply on its square base, dominating the desert scene. Four 91-step stairways, one on each pyramid face, allowed priests to reach the temple at the top. Perhaps the number of steps was related to the 365-day Central American calendar. Now, the stairs are used by tourists who sometimes get dizzy and have to grab a support rope for balance. Some people call the pyramid the *Castillo*, or castle. Others prefer to call the pyramid *Kukulkán*, after the legendary leader of the Toltecs, who built the pyramid.

The students wanted to calculate the height of Kukulkán's pyramid. They had a tape to measure distances, and a homemade quadrant to read angles. Of course, they could not measure lengths in the interior of the pyramid. So they chose sighting points at the nearby Temple of Warriors, points that were 37 m apart. From each sighting point, they measured the angle of sight to the top of the pyramid. The angles they found were 15° and 11.4°. How tall was the pyramid to the nearest meter?

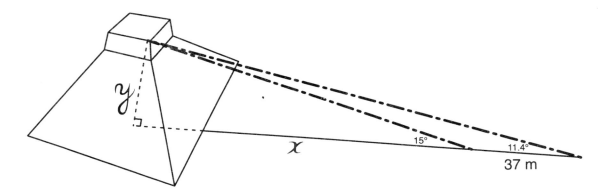

Geometry Activities from Many Cultures

Trigonometry in Babylonia

A Babylonian clay tablet from about 1800 B.C.E. contained the following columns of numbers. The numbers seemed uninteresting until mathematicians realized that the values satisfied the right triangle theorem. Here was proof that the right triangle theorem was known over 1000 years before Pythagoras.

Further analysis shows that the Babylonians had also begun the study of trigonometry. Consider the ratios for c/b. In a right triangle, the ratio c/b is sec A.

a	b	c	c/b	$\sec^{-1} c/b$
120	119	169		
3456	3367	4825		
4800	4601	6649		
13500	12709	18541		
72	65	97		
360	319	481		
2700	2291	3541		
960	799	1249		
600	481	769		
6480	4961	8161		
60	45	75		
2400	1679	2929		
240	161	289		
2700	1771	3229		
90	56	106		

(*Note:* In this table, the broken column for *a* has been restored using the formula, $c^2 = a^2 + b^2$.)

Group Project:
Divide the rows among members of your group. Fill in the column for c/b. Use the $1/x$ key to get b/c. Then using the $\cos^{-1}$ key on your scientific calculator, fill out the last column in the above table. Do you see a pattern in the order of the rows?

Geometry Activities from Many Cultures

Name _____

Date _____

Indian and Islamic Trigonometry

Trigonometry was first used to help build pyramids and survey land. The greatest demand for trigonometry came from the astronomers. From Ptolemy in Egypt to Ulugh Beg in Central Asia, astronomers developed trigonometry to help chart the skies. Ptolemy, working in Egypt about the year 150 C.E., calculated the equivalent of a sine table for angles in steps of ½ degree.

After Ptolemy, major advances in trigonometry were made in India. Then the Islamic mathematicians, from Spain in the West to Iran in the East, expanded Indian trigonometry to include all six common functions: sine, cosine, tangent, cotangent, secant, and cosecant. To illustrate these functions, the ancient astronomers used circles and spheres. Their trigonometry was based on arcs and chords in a circle. As you will see in the explorations that follow, their results also apply to right triangles.

Exploration 1

MATERIALS: compass, protractor, cm scale or graph paper with small squares, calculator

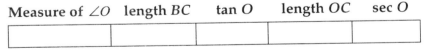

Work with a partner. Check off each step as you complete it.

❏ 1. With a compass, draw a large circle of radius 1, centered at *O*. Draw an acute central angle, *AOB*.

❏ 2. Draw a line tangent to the circle at *B*.

❏ 3. Extend radius $\overline{OA}$ until it intersects the line that is tangent to the circle at *B*. Label the point of intersection *C*.

❏ 4. With your protractor measure ∠*O*. Using *OB* as 1 unit, measure *BC* and *OC*. Record your measurements in the space provided below.

❏ 5. Use your calculator to find tan *O* and sec *O*. To find sec *O*, find cos *O*. Then find the inverse by using the 1/*x* key. Record your readings below.

Measure of ∠O	length BC	tan O	length OC	sec O

Discussion

Do you see any connection between the length *BC* and tan *O*? Explain.

Do you see any connection between the length *OC* and sec *O*? Explain.

(continued)

Geometry Activities from Many Cultures

Indian and Islamic Trigonometry *(continued)*

The early Indian and Islamic astronomers developed their trigonometry working with circles and half chords. In the following activity, you will explore possible similarities and differences between the length of half chords and the sines of angles.

Exploration 2

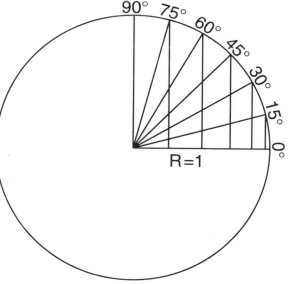

MATERIALS

    compass, protractor, ruler, scientific calculator, graph paper with large squares divided into tenths

Work with a partner. Check off each step as you complete it.

❏   1. With your compass, draw a circle on graph paper with some convenient, large radius, such as twice the side of two large graph paper squares. Use your protractor to help you locate radii to form central angles 15° apart, from 0° to 90°.

❏   2. From the circle, at the endpoints of the radii you drew in step 1, draw segments perpendicular to the horizontal axis. Use vertical graph paper lines as your guide.

❏   3. Complete the following table by measuring the length of the segments you drew in step 2. The radius is a 1-unit length. If your radius is the length of 20 small squares, the length of 2 small squares is 0.1 unit. Find the sine values with your calculator.

❏   4. Discuss any differences or similarities between half chord and sine of the angle.

Measure of angle, degrees	Length of half-chord	Sine of angle
0	0	0
15		
30		
45		
60		
75		
90	1	1

Geometry Activities from Many Cultures

Circumference of the Earth

Al-Biruni was a Central Asian from Khwarizm, like his famous predecessor, al-Khwarizmi. The wars in his country around 1019 C.E. forced al-Biruni to do a lot of traveling. He completed eight books by the age of 30 although he spent most of his twenties fleeing from the wars. When the king demanded that al-Biruni enter government service, he could not refuse. As he wrote, "I was compelled to participate in worldly affairs, which excited the envy of fools, but made the wise pity me." His forced travels took him to Afghanistan and India.

On top of a tall mountain in India, al-Biruni got the idea of a new method of calculating the circumference of the earth. He wanted a method that did not require "walking across hot, dusty deserts."

From the top of the mountain, whose height he knew, al-Biruni sighted the dip angle $\angle BET$. Then he used the law of sines.

$$\frac{EL}{\sin \angle EML} = \frac{LM}{\sin \angle MEL}$$

Since EL, the height of the mountain, and all the angles are known, LM is found by the law of sines. Then $MT = LM$ because they are tangents to the circle from point M, and EM is found using the right triangle theorem. Finally, OT, the radius of the earth can be found from:

$$\frac{ET}{\sin O} = \frac{OT}{\angle TEO}$$

Discussion

The final result for the circumference of the earth was the equivalent of 56 miles/degree. What is the correct value? Al-Biruni's theory was perfect. What measurements could have been a source of error?

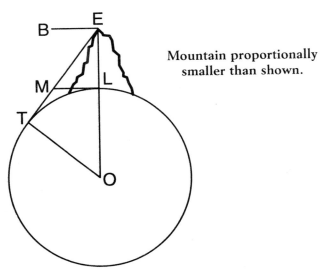

Mountain proportionally
smaller than shown.

Geometry Activities from Many Cultures

The Law of Sines Proved

The Islamic mathematician-astronomers of central Asia made a huge contribution to trigo-nometry. For years they used the Law of Sines to solve practical problems. The first actual proof was given by Nasir-al-Din al-Tusi (1201–1274). He also played a role in the development of a new type of geometry used to study gravity and space-time. Nasir al-Din's son, of the same name, also became a mathematician. The son continued his father's work and wrote books in defense of his father's writings.

Nasir al-Din helped create trigonometry as a special subject; before his time it was considered part of astronomy. In fact, the Islamic astronomers of Asia, Africa, and Spain developed most of the trigonometric formulas we use today. The Mongol invasion and destruction of Baghdad in 1256 set back al-Din's work. However, he was able to return to work when the Mongol ruler Hulagu had a new observatory built for him.

AL-DIN'S PROOF OF THE LAW OF SINES.

This proof is based on the properties of similar triangles. For any triangle ABC, extend $\overline{AB}$ to D, and $\overline{CB}$ to E until both $\overline{AD}$ and $\overline{CE}$ have length equal to an arbitrary unit that we'll call 1. From E, B, and D, drop perpendiculars to the base (extended if needed.) Corresponding sides of similar triangles provide the proportions stated in the law of sines. Since $\sin A = DH/AD$, and $AD = 1$, $\sin A = DH$. Similarly, $\sin C = EF$.

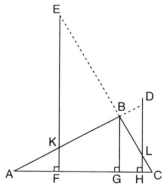

Since $\triangle ABG \sim \triangle ADH$, $DH/AD = BG/AB$. Cross-multiply: $DH \bullet AB = BG \bullet AD$

Since $\triangle BCG \sim \triangle EFC$, $EF/EC = BG/BC$. Cross-multiply: $EF \bullet BC = BG \bullet EC$

Recall that $EC = AD = 1$. So $DH \bullet AB = BG$, and $EF \bullet BC = BG$.

Divide both sides by $BC \bullet AB$ to get $DH/BC = EF/AB$.

Substitute $\sin A = DH$, and $\sin C = EF$. Finally, let $a = BC$, $c = AB$, to get:

$$\frac{\sin A}{a} = \frac{\sin C}{c}$$

In a similar manner it can be shown that: $\dfrac{\sin B}{b} = \dfrac{\sin A}{a} = \dfrac{\sin C}{c}$

(continued)

Geometry Activities from Many Cultures

THE TRIGONOMETRY OF ISLAMIC ASTRONOMERS
Questions for Critical Thinking

1. From about the year 800 to 1500, Islamic astronomers developed most of the trigonometry that we cover in high school classes today. Why do you think astronomers needed trigonometry?

2. During the Middle Ages, many astronomers earned their living as astrologers. Today astrology is not recognized as a science. What do you think is the difference between astronomy and astrology?

3. Al-Biruni used the law of sines to calculate the circumference of the earth. That was before the law of sines had been proved. Do you think al-Biruni was wrong to use the law of sines before it had been proved? Can you think of similar present day examples?

4. What type of geometry problems can be solved by use of the law of sines?

5. Al-Biruni calculated about 56 miles/degree of a great circle around the earth.
   (a) Given 360° in a circle, what was his estimate of the circumference of the earth?

   (b) How large was his error? What do you think caused his error?

6. A vertical stone pillar in Ethiopia stood on a hill that made a 14° angle with the horizontal. At a time of day when the angle of elevation of the sun was 55°, the stone pillar cast a shadow that was 18.3 m long. How high was the stone pillar? How long a shadow would a stone pillar of the same height cast if it were standing on a horizontal site instead of a hill?

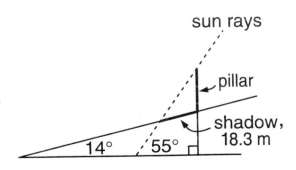

Multicultural Origins of Logical Proof

Al-Biruni used the law of sines to calculate the circumference of the earth. That was 200 years before the law was actually *proved*. The history of calculus was similar. Calculus was first used for practical needs. Only later was it placed on a logical basis.

Today all new mathematics must be proved. New mathematics is often discovered by exploring a proof. There are famous *conjectures* that people think are true but are not yet proved. For example, the Goldbach Conjecture of 1742 has been tested for numbers past 100,000. But it still has not been proved true for all even whole numbers. It states: Every even whole number can be expressed as the sum of two primes.

Logic and proof are not limited to mathematics. Every culture has its system of laws. There is a system of proof for those accused of violating a law. An interesting example comes from ancient Egypt in a 4000-year old story, "The Story of the Eloquent Peasant."

The peasant is robbed by an assistant to High Steward Rensi. He goes to Rensi for justice and makes such an eloquent argument that Rensi decides to notify the king. The king is delighted at the report and wants to hear more. So he secretly sends food to the man and his family while the trial continues. The trial goes on for 9 days and every word is recorded for the pleasure of the king. The peasant starts out with flattery.

For you are father to the orphan,

Husband to the widow,

Brother to the rejected woman . . . Leader free of greed.

When it appears that flattery is getting him nowhere, the peasant changes tactics:

You are like a town without a mayor,

Like a troop without a leader,

Like a ship without a captain,

A company without a chief.

You are a sheriff who steals

After the ninth day of speeches, justice is finally done. The peasant has his goods returned. The thief is punished and his goods are given to the peasant.

Group Discussion

1. Select a trial that has been covered in detail in the newspapers and discuss what logical arguments, or lack of logic you have noticed in the trial arguments. Was justice done?

2. Find some examples of even numbers that are a sum of two primes. Do these examples prove the conjecture for all even numbers?

Geometry Activities from Many Cultures

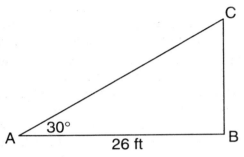

Banneker and the Law of Sines

Benjamin Banneker was an African American astronomer on the survey team that planned Washington, D.C., in 1791. He was an extraordinary genius. He had never seen a trigonometry book until the age of 57 when a neighbor loaned him astronomy books and instruments. In a year, he taught himself astronomy. Here are some of his practice problems.

"**Trigonometry**
The base being given, and the acute angle at *A*, to find the hypotenuse and perpendicular –"

The diagram to the right is similar to the one Banneker drew in his journal. The information it gives for right triangle *ABC* is that *AB* is 26 feet, and angle *A* measures 30°. Find *AC* and *BC*. Notice that in Banneker's diagram, ∠*B* is the right angle. Work along with Banneker by filling in the blanks.

Method 1: Construction

Check off each step as you complete it.

❑ 1. Draw a diagram to scale, on graph paper. Draw *AB* = 26 units.

❑ 2. With a protractor, draw a right angle at *B* and a 30° angle at *A*. Extend the sides of these angles until they intersect at *C*.

❑ 3. Count the number of units in *AC* and *BC*, using a strip of graph paper as your scale.

   AC = _____ units. *BC* = _____ units.

Method 2: Law of Sines

Banneker did not have calculators or computers. Astronomers of those times used logarithms to speed up their work. We can follow Banneker's method using our scientific calculators.

Given right △*ABC*, with right angle at *B*, *AB* = 26 ft, ∠*A* = 30°. Then ∠*C* = _____.

Use the law of sines to find *BC*.

$$\frac{BC}{\sin 30°} = \frac{26 \text{ ft}}{\sin 60°} \quad BC = \underline{\hspace{2cm}} \text{ ft}$$

$$\frac{AC}{\sin 90°} = \frac{26 \text{ ft}}{\sin 60°} \quad AC = \underline{\hspace{2cm}} \text{ ft}$$

Method 3

Sides of a 30° – 60° – 90° triangle are in the ratio of 1 : $\sqrt{3}$: 2. So 1 : *BC* = $\sqrt{3}$: 26. Once you find *BC*, double it to get *AC*. *BC* = _____. *AC* = _____.

Geometry Activities from Many Cultures

Trigonometry and Nursing—
The Story of Florence Nightingale

Florence Nightingale saved the lives of thousands in British military hospitals during the Crimean war of 1854 to 1855. This was before antibiotics were used, even before the germ theory of infection was generally accepted. She achieved a dramatic reduction in the mortality rates, or death rates, by putting into effect basic sanitary reforms. In just one year after Nightingale's reforms, the death rate dropped from 578 deaths to 17 per 1,000.

When the war ended, Nightingale realized that many more lives could be saved around the world if hospitals were cleaned up. She knew that people had the power to pressure governments for hospital reform. And she had the statistics to prove her case. But how could she present the statistics in a way that would command attention?

Nightingale decided to use colorful graphs to illustrate the need for hospital reform. She even invented polar-area diagrams to dramatize her cause. Fortunately, she had the background in trigonometry and algebra she needed. In those days very few women were allowed to study mathematics. Friends and relatives had also tried to discourage her from going into nursing because it was not considered "respectable." Florence Nightingale overcame the prejudice to make a great contribution to the sciences of medicine and statistics.

Project

Make and compare two graphs: a polar-area graph, and a line-graph of "Mortality Rate at a Military Hospital During the Crimean War."

MATERIALS: Rectangular coordinate graph paper; polar coordinate graph paper—or make your own with protractor, compass, ruler, and calculator.

Check off each step as you complete it.

❑ 1. On polar coordinate paper, divide the 360° scale into 52 equal parts to represent the weeks in the year. For simplicity, start Oct. Week 1 at 7°. Then Oct. Week 2 would be 7° + (360°/52). Use the constant addend feature of your calculator and round off readings to the nearest degree.

❑ 2. Plot the polar coordinates from the table on the next page. Connect the points with straight line segments to make a polar area graph.

❑ 3. Color in the area plotted.

❑ 4. Complete the table for the rectangular coordinates. Make the x-coordinate the time elapsed in weeks, starting with "Oct. Week 1" as 1. Hint: Most months have more than 4 weeks.

❑ 5. Plot coordinates (x, y) from your table. Connect the points to make a broken-line graph.

❑ 6. Compare the two graphs for eye appeal and effectiveness.

(continued)

Name _____

Date _____

Trigonometry and Nursing—
The Story of Florence Nightingale (continued)

Mortality Rate at a British Military Hospital, 1854-5
(Adapted from an 800-page report by Florence Nightingale)

	Coordinates for polar-area graph		Coordinates for line graph	
	Mortality Rate, % *	Time elapsed, weeks	Time elapsed, weeks	Mortality Rate, %
Week	**r**	**θ, in degrees**	**x**	**y**
Oct. Week 1	140	7	_____	140
Oct. Week 4	103	28	_____	103
Nov. Week 4	128	55	_____	128
Dec. Week 3	203	76	_____	203
Jan. Week 1	216	97	_____	216
Jan. Week 2	305	104	_____	305
Feb. Week 1	415	125	_____	415
Mar. Week 1	215	152	_____	215
Apr. Week 1	123	187	_____	123
Apr. Week 2	81	194	_____	81
May Week 2	53	222	_____	53
Jun. Week 2	47	249	_____	47
Jun. Week 4	40	263	_____	40

* The mortality rate is based on the number of patients in the hospital. In any given week, if patients die soon after admission and are immediately replaced by new patients, the mortality rate can go over 100 percent. In February 1855 the rate reached 415 percent.

Questions for Critical Thinking

1. Compare the two graphs. Which do you think would be most eye-catching? Which is easier to understand?

2. Judging from the above table, when do you think the hospital reforms began?

3. In many countries most nurses are men. In other countries, most nurses are women. Do you think that gender should be a factor in any profession, whether nursing or mathematics?

Geometry Activities from Many Cultures

Resources

Arnold, Dieter. *Building in Egypt.* New York: Oxford Press, 1991.

Ascher, Marcia. *Ethnomathematics.* New York: Brooks Cole, 1991.

Berggren, J.L. *Episodes in the Mathematics of Medieval Islam.* New York: Springer Verlag, 1980.

Boyer, Carl. *A History of Mathematics.* New York: John Wiley, 1968.

Chace, Arnold B. *The Rhind Mathematical Papyrus.* Reston, VA: NCTM, 1979. Translation of ancient Egyptian mathematics text, c 1800 B.C.E.

Closs, Michael P., ed. *Native American Mathematics.* Austin: University of Texas Press, 1986.

Gerdes, Paulus. *Women and Geometry in Southern Africa.* Maputo, Mozambique: Universidade Pedagogica Mocambique, 1995.

—— *Sipatsi, Technology, Art and Geometry in Inhambane.* Maputo, Mozambique: Instituto Superior Pedagogico Mocambique, 1994.

—— *Lusona, Geometrical Recreations of Africa.* Maputo, Mozambique: African Mathematical Union and Instituto Superior Pedagogico Mocambique, 1991, PO Box 257, Maputo, Mozambique.

Gillings, Richard J. *Mathematics in the Time of the Pharaohs.* Cambridge, MA: MIT Press, 1975. Dover reprint, 1982.

Joseph, George Gheverghese. *The Crest of the Peacock: Non-European Roots of Mathematics.* London: Tauris, 1991.

Katz, Victor. *A History of Mathematics.* New York: Harpers Collins College, 1993.

Lumpkin, Beatrice, with Dorothy Strong. *Multicultural Science and Math Connections: Middle School Projects and Activities.* Portland, Maine: J. Weston Walch, Publisher, 1995.

—— with Arthur B. Powell. *Math—A Rich Heritage.* Upper Saddle River, NJ: Globe Fearon, 1995.

Multiculturalism in Mathematics, Science and Technology. Menlo Park: Addison-Wesley, 1992.

Powell, Arthur B. and Marilyn Frankenstein, eds. *Ethnomathematics: Challenging Eurocentrism in Mathematics Education.* Albany, NY: State University of New York, 1997.

Swetz, Frank, and T.I. Kao. *Was Pythagoras Chinese?* University Park, PA: Pennsylvania State University Press, 1977.

Yan, Li, and Shiran Du. *Chinese Mathematics—A Concise History.* tr. John N. Crossley, and Anthony W.C. Lun. Oxford: Clarendon, 1987. (Technical, excellent.)

Zaslavsky, Claudia. *Africa Counts.* Westport, CN, Lawrence Hill, 1979.

—— *Fear of Math.* New Brunswick, N.J.: Rutgers University Press, 1994.

—— *The Multicultural Math Classroom.* Portsmouth, NH: Heinemann, 1995.

Professional Study Groups in Multicultural Mathematics

AMUCHA (African Mathematical Union Commission on the History of Mathematics in Africa). Chairperson, Paulus Gerdes. C.P. 3276, Maputo, MOZAMBIQUE.paulus@up.uem.mz

Benjamin Banneker Association. An educators' organization devoted to the improvement of mathematics education of African American students. President Dr. Carol Malloy, 1125 Anderson St., Durham, NC 22705. cmalloy@email.unc.edu

HPM (International Study Group on the Relations of History to the Pedagogy of Mathematics). Chairperson of the Americas Section, Victor Katz, University of the District of Columbia, Washington, DC 20008.vkatz@udc.edu

ISGEm (International Study Group on Ethnomathematics). President Ubi D'Ambrosio, Rua Peixoto Giomide 1772 ap. 83, 01409-002, Sao Paulo, SP BRAZIL.Ubi@usp.br

Index

Share Your Bright Ideas with Us!

We want to hear from you! Your valuable comments and suggestions will help us meet your current and future classroom needs.

Your name_____Date_____

School name_____Phone_____

School address_____

Grade level taught_____Subject area(s) taught_____Average class size_____

Where did you purchase this publication?_____

Was your salesperson knowledgeable about this product?   Yes_____   No_____

What monies were used to purchase this product?

____School supplemental budget   ____Federal/state funding   ____Personal

Please "grade" this Walch publication according to the following criteria:

Quality of service you received when purchasing ....A   B   C   D   F
Ease of use...A   B   C   D   F
Quality of content..A   B   C   D   F
Page layout ....A   B   C   D   F
Organization of material ....A   B   C   D   F
Suitability for grade level ....A   B   C   D   F
Instructional value...A   B   C   D   F

COMMENTS:_____

_____

What specific supplemental materials would help you meet your current—or future—instructional needs?

_____

Have you used other Walch publications? If so, which ones?_____

May we use your comments in upcoming communications?   ____Yes   ____No

Please **FAX** this completed form to **207-772-3105**, or mail it to:

Product Development, J. Weston Walch, Publisher, P.O. Box 658, Portland, ME 04104-0658

We will send you a **FREE GIFT** as our way of thanking you for your feedback.   **THANK YOU!**